SHADOWED HOURGLASS

SHADOWED HOURGLASS

A Collection of Poetry and Prose

LUW PRESS

Contents

SHADOWED HOURGLASS
A Collection of Poetry and Prose
Copyright © 2021 LUW Press

Print ISBN: 978-1-7354841-0-5

Cover design by Lauren Makena

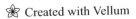 Created with Vellum

Experience is a jewel, and it had need be so, for it is often purchased at an infinite rate.
-William Shakespeare

Eiderdown
LORRAINE JEFFERY

Eating a slow breakfast.
Under apple trees we planted
on the deck you built.

Surrounded by salmon roses,
lemon lilies, raspberries,
rhubarb's magenta sprays.

Our eiderdown speech
matches birdsong,
bees mask traffic buzz.

No playful sideways glance;
our shadowed hourglass flows
wistful—memory etched.

We smile, stroll crumbling brick
paths you laid long ago, warm,
in bone-deep companionship,

holding this bedazzled morning
in our blue-veined hands.

Me and Liz

JOSIE HUME

"Fine," Liz says, storming into the bedroom. A hint of bleach follows her. She's been cleaning again. Whenever she gets worked up, she cleans. "You win, all right? I've decided to go."

"Whatever," I say. If I had a nickel for every time she'd 'decided to do it' and then chickened out at the last minute… Well, I'd take them to the bank because those Coinstar machines are a total rip off. I'd been nagging her again to see a therapist while we walked home from school. She hates when I do that. I hate when I do it, too—the therapist is a total hag—but talking to a trained hag would be better than not talking to anyone.

"I mean it this time," Liz says. "I still think it's a mistake, but if you really want me to, I'll talk to Dr. Stevens."

I flip another page of a teen glamour magazine. I'm on my stomach, sprawled across her bed. Liz and I have been best friends since forever—well, since kindergarten anyway, which was like, eleven years ago. So, yeah. Forever. I know her better than I know myself. She'll chicken out again. I love her, but she's been dragging her feet about seeing a therapist for the last

five months, ever since she started working for Dr. Stevens. I see
no reason why I should believe her this time.

She tosses her long blonde hair over her shoulder. "You don't
seem very excited that I've finally decided to listen to your
words of wisdom."

I can totally hear the air quotes around those last three words.
"I'm partying on the inside," I say. I flip another page. Out of the
corner of my eye, I watch her fume next to the bed—hands on
hips, eyebrows slammed over her eyes. I know all her moods. I
call this one 'pissed: in your face'. "Look at this." I roll over and
hold up the mag so she can see the article. "You can use a toilet
seat cover to blot your makeup. Brilliant! Let's grab a few from
school tomorrow. Cha-ching. Money in the bank."

She doesn't think I'm funny. She stomps over to her laptop,
slams into the desk chair, and starts pounding on the keyboard.

I'm still pretending I'm absorbed in the gross-out makeup
tips some twenty-something idiot typed up and some should-
have-known-better magazine actually printed, but my eyes are
wandering. I practically live in this room. The pink walls that she
outgrew seven years ago are covered with retro posters I helped
pick out—a killer Michael Jackson in black and white from
before he went weird, a sixties kaleidoscope Peace poster, a
couple Dr Who posters because we're geeks (David Tennent, of
course), a few emo ones from our blue period, and this wicked-
awesome Spiderman poster where his shadow is a spider (okay,
that one's not retro, but it was too cool to pass up).

I keep telling her to talk to her mom about repainting—or,
hey, buying a new comforter that doesn't have a ballet Barbie on
it—but she keeps ignoring me about that, too. It's not that her
mom doesn't love her. Kind of. Her mom's just busy smoking
and drinking and doesn't seem to have a lot of time to redecorate.

Or do the dishes.

Or remember she has a daughter.

So, I try to spend as much time with Liz as I can. It sucks to be lonely. Trust me, I know. I was lonely before I found Liz. Plus, kids can be cruel. A lot of the 'good' kids at school don't want to be friends with someone who smells like smoke and wears secondhand clothes (we prefer the term 'preloved'). That's how we got to be friends in the first place. Nicholas Peterson (or as I like to call him, Nick the Prick) was as big a loser in kindergarten as he is in high school. After a brutal game of four square, where Liz kicked his trash, he said Liz smelled like an ashtray and looked like she crawled out of the dumpster—not even original. The other kids laughed.

Liz looked so sad that I stepped up. And I've stood beside her every day since. We're inseparable, like two boobs in a bra.

I tip my head back and look at the screen. She's pulled up some YouTube video about dog fails, and I watch a chihuahua chase a tennis ball across a trampoline for a few seconds before I sit up with a sigh. "Stop wasting time. Call Dr. Stevens."

"Can this really be called wasting time?" She gestures to the screen where a teacup Pomeranian is trying to climb out of an oversized coffee mug. "Besides, I don't know her office number."

"You don't need to call her office. She gave you her personal number like two months ago when you picked up her poodle. I watched you type it into your phone." I point to the phone lying on the desk next to her laptop. Exhibit A.

She doesn't say anything, but I know she heard me because her shoulders climb up to her ears.

"C'mon. You gotta do it," I say.

"She's my boss. It'd be too weird."

"She's not your 'boss'. You walk her dog—that's different. And not to be rude or anything, but the fact that you work for her is the only reason you can afford to see a therapist at all, even a jerk like Dr. Stevens."

"If you don't like her so much, then why are you pushing me to see her? In fact, why do I even need to talk to someone else? I've got you." She sends me a big sloppy smile. "You always listen."

"I *am* a good listener. And I *do* give brilliant advice." I lean toward her. "Which is why you should listen to me when I say, I am not qualified to help you. Your problems are bigger than two sixteen-year-olds can handle."

"What problems?" she asks defensively.

"Um, like your home life is a total disaster." I hold up a finger. "Your mom ignores you when she bothers to pull herself out of a bottle long enough to even notice you're there." Another finger. "And," finger number three goes up, "you live in a pile of junk."

"Hey!"

"It's *clean* junk," I say, softening the blow. And it is. There are lots of things she can't control, but what she can, she's a Nazi about. Her room is spotless, and she keeps the rest of the trailer smelling like the detergent aisle at the grocery store. She even follows her mom around with a broom and a dustpan to sweep up the ash and trash her mom drops everywhere. It drives her mom nuts. Good, is what I say.

"And don't even get me started on your daddy issues," I say.

"I don't even remember my dad. How can I have issues?"

I roll my eyes. "That's *why* you have issues."

"Okay, well a lot of people have problems with their families. Are all of them talking to therapists?"

"They *should* be. Add being bullied at school—"

"I'm not bullied anymore."

"Only because you have gone to great—some might even say ridiculous—lengths to remain invisible."

She sticks her tongue out at me. She knows I'm one of the 'some' who would say ridiculous.

"Then, there're your grades, your borderline OCD, your paralyzation about the future—"

"That's not a word."

"—your lack of self-esteem…" I wave eight fingers in her face. "I'm running out of fingers. Need I go on?"

"Fine." Her arms are folded tight across her chest—classic defense pose.

"Fine." I mirror her posture, except mine is less about defense and more like the captain of a spaceship who just ordered his men to crush the enemy with their overwhelming fire power. "Then make the call."

"It's just… Are you sure you want me to?"

"Have I not been arguing—"

"Nagging."

"—with you to go ever since Dr. Stevens offered to talk to you for free?"

"I know, but… Never mind. I guess if you're sure there's no reason not to go." She snatches her phone off the desk. Her thumbs flash across the screen.

I hear a tinny murmur on the other end, then, "Hi, Dr. Stevens. This is Liz, I walk—" Another murmur. "That's right." Relief. "You said I could talk to you if I ever—" More chatter. A smile. "Yeah." Then, "Okay." Then more talking. "Tomorrow. After school." Talking, talking. "Yeah, I know where it is. I, um, googled you." Talking. *Still* talking. Lots of talking. I yawn. Finally, "Okay. Sounds good. Thanks. I'll see you tomorrow." She hangs up.

"So…"

"So, I'm going to her office tomorrow after school. She said she was glad I called."

"And…"

"And you were right. I do need to talk to someone. Thanks."

"And…" I make a 'give it to me' motion with my hands.

She rolls her eyes again. We do that a lot. We're teenagers, it's in our contract. "And you're the smartest person in the world and the best friend I could ever ask for. You're the master commander, the king kong, the captain my captain, the—"

"Okay, now you're just being ridiculous." Then I get serious. "I'm really glad you called."

"Don't be glad yet," she says. It sounds like a warning.

I frown, but before I can ask what she means, she says, "I guess I'd better get busy on that English Lit paper."

My cue to leave. I stand up. "Do you want me to come with you tomorrow?" She hesitates. "I mean, for moral support. I'll just sit out in the lobby."

She smiles. "That'd be great. I'll see you tomorrow morning?"

"Sure. I'll meet you at the gym. We can walk to school together."

"Sounds good. See you then."

She pulls up her doc, and I slip away.

I'm waiting for her outside the gym the next morning. She always does a workout, but that's mostly just a formality. The main reason she goes to the gym is to shower and change. She rents a locker where she keeps seven shirts and four pants, painstakingly chosen from thrift shops all over town. Twenty-eight outfits, she always says. Plus a few scarves and vests, things like that, to mix it up.

Twenty-eight outfits that don't smell like smoke.

I can tell she's nervous by the way her eyes dart everywhere and the fact that she's hurrying. She never hurries to school. She always times it exactly right to get into her seat thirty seconds before the bell rings. Early might mean she'd have to talk to someone, late would mean attention. Plus, she's already got her backpack on, full to the brim and so heavy I'm pretty sure she's shrunk an inch since starting high school. That's one of the ridiculous ways she avoids people—she doesn't use her locker.

School is the usual snooze fest. Liz likes it—but then, she's a genius. She doesn't get genius grades (again, that would attract attention), but if her teachers weren't the clueless noobs they are, they'd realize it's pretty weird for someone to get exactly eighty percent on every single assignment. You'd think a math teacher would notice something like that—maybe realize that student is a lot smarter than a B. But her teachers are as dense as everyone else in that school. She has a lot to offer, if anyone besides me bothered to look.

After school, we walk the few blocks to the therapist's office. The temperature is still brisk, but spring has finally decided to make an appearance. The air holds a hint of green, and there's a feeling of anticipation, like nature is holding her breath waiting to see what happens next.

Or maybe that's just me. I look over at Liz and catch another worried glance she throws my way. She's been doing that all day. No wonder my insides are tangled up like a pair of earbuds in the dryer. (Drying earbuds ruins them, by the way. Or maybe that was the wash cycle?) I've seen her nervous before. This looks worse. Much worse.

"Are you doing okay?" I ask, mostly because I'm not. She's got me second guessing myself, wondering if this was such a good idea.

"I'm nervous." She fidgets with her backpack for a minute then says, "Will you come in with me? I mean, into my appointment?"

"Are you sure?"

"I think so."

"Don't you think your therapist will have a problem with that?"

"I think she'll be okay." She looks at me. "Please?"

What do you say when your best friend says she needs you? "Yeah, I'll come." But I wish I could say no. I'm not sure what has her jumpier than a flea on a hot plate, but it's wigging me out. Something's wrong for sure. If Liz didn't want to go so bad, she should have ignored me. What do I know, anyway? I'm just a kid.

By the time we get to the office, I'm a mess. My hands are shaking, my stomach pitching, my chest so tight I'm surprised I haven't cracked a rib. I scowl at the discreet sign outside the door before slinking into the waiting room. A few demure chairs surround a tabled pastel flower arrangement. An obligatory ficus stands in one corner. Soft music plays over invisible speakers.

I pretty much hate it. No matter how fancy it's dressed up, the room still feels heavy from all the baggage people have lugged into it. The oppression strangles me, and I have to force myself to sit down in front of the cliché fake flowers.

We don't have to wait long before a door opens and a woman in a pantsuit comes out. Who invented pantsuits, anyway? They automatically categorize you as 'old lady'. I will never wear one. Even when I'm President.

I've seen the woman before, but I've never met her. The high and mighty Dr. Stevens. She's just plain stuck up, if you ask me. I always stay back and wait on the sidewalk while Liz goes up the front walk to pick up her precious poodle, but she's never said hi to me. Not once. Who does that? I don't care if you're busy, it's just common decency. If she hadn't volunteered to talk to Liz for free, I'd be tempted to tell her what I think of her.

"Thanks for seeing me, Dr. Stevens," Liz says.

"Call me Susan," the woman says, smiling at Liz. "Come in." She doesn't offer to shake hands. That's good. My hands are ice cold and sweaty.

I trail after the 'good' doctor. Her office doesn't look anything like an office. It looks like a home, with a comfy floral couch and a few chairs. There's even a TV and a small kitchenette. Slick, but I'm not fooled. I'm on my guard, ready to jump in and stop the conversation the second Liz needs me.

I sink into one corner of the couch, and Liz perches on the edge at the other end. 'Call me Susan' takes a chair. She folds her hands in her lap and smiles. "I'm so glad you called me, Liz. I had a feeling you could use someone to talk to." They chit chat for bit, and I zone out, wishing I could drink some Pepto-Bismol or something. I bet Dr. Stevens wouldn't like it if I puked all over her sofa. She couldn't very well ignore me then. I tune back in when she asks, "What would you like to discuss?"

I wait for Liz to say her mom or school, but she says, "I think I'm crazy."

I blink.

I'm not the only one. I can see Susan trying to figure that one out, too.

"I'm serious," Liz says. "I think I'm really crazy."

Susan frowns. If I were her friend, I'd call that her 'gently confused' look. I bet she practices it in the mirror. I bet she thinks it makes her patients less uncomfortable. It doesn't. "That's a word I don't use very often in my line of work. I usually find it's too vague. Do you mind telling me what you mean when you say you're crazy?"

The hair on my arms is standing straight up. I'm wondering the same thing.

Liz shoots me a look so full of misery and apology that my heart crawls into my throat. I know it's bad—whatever she's going to say—and I don't want to hear it.

"It's my best friend," she says.

My stomach is a tight knot. My mind races over the last few days, weeks... What did I do? What did I say? We tell each other everything—at least I thought we did. What can Liz say to Susan that she can't say to me?

"What's wrong with your best friend?" Susan asks.

Liz rubs her hands on her knees. "Nothing. She's perfect."

Relief wars with nausea. Nausea wins. Perfect is supposed to be good, right? Then how come I feel worse? I know I'm not perfect. *Liz* knows I'm not perfect. Did she mean perfect for her? Like I'm the yin to her yang? I try to be a good friend. I—

Susan interrupts my spinning thoughts. "Why don't you tell me about her."

Liz bites her lip, and I can literally see her gather her courage. Whatever she's going to say is scary—huge scary—and she's worried how Susan will take it. I get ready to go all mama bear at the first sign of disrespect from the doctor.

But instead of looking at Susan, Liz looks straight at me. "You want to know about my best friend?" Her eyes are begging my forgiveness.

Then realization strikes. She's not worried how Susan will take it. She's worried about me. We're in a therapist's office for *me*. I'm not the mediator between Liz and Susan. Susan's the mediator.

The attack is so unexpected, I can't build my defenses. It feels like my skin is missing, like my nerves are exposed. My heart is racing. My fingers and toes start to tingle. I feel like I'm floating away, like nothing is real, like I'm in someone else's dream.

I look into her eyes. "Don't say it," I whisper. "Don't ruin this. Don't make me go away."

But she doesn't listen. "The first thing you need to know about my best friend is she's imaginary."

Sunshine Walls
JAYROD P. GARRETT

Against a backdrop of sunshine
ninja turtles fought
sorcery while electric tape ninjas
built box skyscrapers filling the skies
of my bedroom. The tang
of ketchup sandwiches –
caviar to my tongue.
It was the landscape of a perfect life.

Mom never took me to the zoo,
each winter we left bread
out for deer. We watched
from the kitchen window,
where our bright eyes met
as the deer grew fat off bread and grass.
I asked if they wanted ketchup.
She told me, deer don't like tomatoes.

That first summer I played Tarzan
I twisted thin leafy vines
together to swing through jungles.
I invited the boys
down the road to come play.
They called me nigger
and said I didn't belong there.
I stopped looking for playmates.

Except when our pastor asked me to join
Scouts. His face lit up speaking of the memories,
so I said yes. I was confused
when the scoutmaster cancelled
our meetings. My fragile faith
burst when the kids at church
told me I didn't belong there,
so Scouts started ten minutes later.

School was no different.
A child saw my skin an invitation
for bruises. I cowered
until one day I struck back.
Nigger was the least of my names then.
Violent, aggressive, angry
written on my permanent record.
I isolated myself on the edge of the playground
staring at the sun. I thought it was beautiful
until it called me blind
and a doctor set glasses on my face.

As a child this was my life.
My only refuge was my home.

And I was glad to see my Mom
hand fistfuls of money to our landlord
for four years to lease to own
this home. Until one day a white car
with white men, with white papers
demanded we move. Or pay them
the money we stole from them
for the past three years.

So I packed my ninjas,
ketchup sandwiches,
into my old skyscrapers.
And we moved to another home
with sunshine walls. When we moved
in I turned the lights out.
I couldn't spend another moment
in the light waiting
for the day it would tell
us, you don't belong.

Patient Zero

AMANDA BARUSCH

"Have you landed??? Did you get the tickets?? Can't wait! XXX"

Kisses in caps. Yum!

Melissa's text perked him up during the forced march through endless airport corridors. He grinned to himself and stopped to reply.

No, better keep the girl waiting . . . build the suspense.

He did have the concert tickets, and they'd cost him two week's pay. He figured Melissa was worth it.

The chick is hot!

Lost in fantasies, he almost missed the sign directing him to screening. His shoes squeaked on the tile as he made a sharp right turn to grab the mandatory form.

He ticked all the right boxes.

No fever.

No cough.

No fatigue—well, some, but that was to be expected after a long flight.

Just check no and sign the bloody thing.

His voice echoed in the plexiglass cubicle. "I feel fine," he said. "Glad to be home. Hey, I just want to crash, mate." He gave what he thought was a charming grin, but the masked technician just rammed a long Q-tip up his nose.

"You'll have the result in 48 hours. Meanwhile, you are required to self-isolate."

"Yes, sir." *No way that's going to happen, bud. I've got a date with Melissa!*

———

Self-isolate. Decades later, the words still echo in his ears. He puts the kettle on for morning tea and wonders whether the neighbor will bring him one of her nice scones. She might pat him on the arm and tell him he's not such a bad sort. Anyway, it's peaceful on a Sunday, no threatening phone calls, no sound but the click click click of the clock and occasional swish of a car racing through the puddles on High Street.

He drifts outside to fetch the paper and stops in his tracks on the way back. Red letters scrawl across the front wall of his house.

Damn.

He grabs the bucket and sets to work, knuckles still cracked from last time. Rain pelts his head and dribbles down his neck. He works himself into a stinky sweat scrubbing the defaced wall.

Red paint. Always so hard to get out.

His hands ache from scrubbing, and now there's a blood-red stain beneath his kitchen window. He can still make out the faint letters: *K I L L E*

It's the truth, ain't it? Can't erase what I am.

He glares at a boy riding by on a bike. He's sure it's the one who defaced his wall.

Youngster wasn't even alive then. Forty bloody years. Will they ever forget?

———————

He puts on his hat, picks up his cane, and leaves for the market.

"Just the flowers?" the checker asks, hers the only human voice he'll hear today.

I'm self-isolating. "Hmm? Oh, yes. Just the flowers, thanks."

He stops at a bench, pulls some twine from his pocket, and assembles the bright peonies into small bouquets, thirteen of them plus one for the neighbor lady. He tosses a flower with a broken stem into the gutter.

The cemetery gate groans open at a nudge from his hand. Hairs rise on the back of his neck and he knows she's there.

Yes.

There she is, gyrating to rock and roll that only she can hear. A thick fog blurs her edges, but he sees her in his mind's eye— glinting blue eyes, curly black strands clinging to her sweaty face, left breast peeking out from that low-cut dress.

Ah, those luscious breasts!

He holds out a bouquet, but she skips away. Her gauzy skirt twists in an ethereal breeze while her high heels click click click with each step on thin air.

Always marking time, that girl.

An icy finger threads a path down his spine, and her hand nestles on his rump like a cat.

"It's too late," she whispers, and a cloud of Scotch engulfs his head.

He turns, but she hides behind a tree. "Too late for what, Melissa?"

"Too late for everything. Your time's up, mate." She licks his ear, and he shivers violently. "Time to pay for your sins."

"But, Melissa, I didn't know I was infected!"

Her laugh whistles through the trees, and she disappears over the gate.

He gives a nervous chuckle and pats his aching chest.

She's just messing with me.

Patient Zero sighs and weaves through the graveyard placing fresh bouquets on thirteen scattered graves, all of them his.

The Islands of the Dead

CARA O'SULLIVAN

On the far side of a corn field,
Grave markers stand as sentinels of the dead,
Holding back the dark, verdant forest
That thrums with the bass of tree frogs
And silences filled by birdsong and hawk cry.
The tombstones are sails full of wind and shadow,
As though the whole cemetery could suddenly rise,
Soaring over prairie, forest, field, and river,
Ascend into the billowing clouds that spread over these
    plains,
As they swell with rain, electricity, and thunder, ready to
    bless
The living with rivers and lakes, with leaping fish and
    singing frogs,
Ready to bless the dead with the lull of raindrops over
    closed eyes,
Bones of bead-wrapped hands. The dead dream of the
    living,

Wishing for them the sweet shushing wind spreading
    circles,

A faint gong on the surface of a pond, where a lone bird
    sings.

A Sense of Justice

JOHNNY WORTHEN

"Just since today?"

Kevan nodded. "Started this morning on the way to work."

The doctor scrolled down his computer screen, scanning Kevan Lamont's medical history. Tennis elbow, ulcer, drug abuse, and chlamydia. Boner pills. Rogaine.

"You're forty-three?" he asked.

"That's what I said."

"You're in good shape. I get a lot of obesity and diabetes."

"Bully for you." Lamont's tone was sharp and condescending, sending the doctor a message.

He got it. "It's not a stroke," he said. "It's not a heart attack. We'll know more when the blood work is done."

"Useless."

"I'm suspecting a migraine."

"My head doesn't hurt," said Lamont, silently cursing his regular physician for being away.

"It doesn't need to." The doctor stood up, anxious to get out of the room. "I'll call you when the blood work comes in. For now, go home and lie down. Stay in a dark room. Cold compress over your eyes."

"Dark room?"

"Yes."

"I have too much work to do," said Lamont, adjusting his Rolex. "I'm with Tomas, Walters, and Lamont. I'm Lamont."

"I've seen your commercials."

"How about some pills?"

There it was, thought the doctor. A drug seeker. A big-time lawyer in a five-thousand-dollar suit hitting up an Urgent Care for some charity on a Wednesday afternoon. He should have seen it coming.

"I'll write you something."

"Something strong."

"I'll give you—wait. Weren't you involved in the Ecoes case?" The association hadn't registered before, and damned if he knew how it had then or why he'd said it out loud.

Lamont stared, dumbfounded. "What in God's name made you say that?"

"I just thought of it," he said, rolling it over in his mind. "I remember when he was executed. It was on the news."

"That was a long time ago. Seven years, for hell's sake," said Lamont, feeling his heart thump against his ribs. "I'm not a public defender anymore. I'm in private practice now."

"Less stress, more money?"

"You bet."

The doctor noted the fresh color in Lamont's cheeks, his ears flushed, his swagger defeated, his eyes seeking empty corners where before they'd bored into him. "Are you having another... Are you alright?"

"You said I am."

The snark was back. "We'll know more when the blood work comes in. Now, go home—"

"Dark room—yeah, yeah. Pills?"

"Of course." Lamont had famously once sued a 7-Eleven for not having fresh coffee. He was not a man to cross. He wrote out a script for a strong painkiller, something with a relaxant. Something to take the edge off, let the man sleep. No refills.

"Lower your stress level if you can." He handed Lamont the paper.

"Yeah, yeah." Lamont took the script and left without a goodbye.

It had first been a smell. An acrid biting stench that stung his nostrils and bit above his eyes. It was the odor of burnt toast, scorched cinnamon, asafoetida. Singed hair. Hot spice stink changing to tropical sewer. Organic. Thick. Cloying. He imagined an overstocked Asian market burning to the ground and searched for smoke along the freeway corridor but saw only traffic. He'd driven that stretch a thousand times and never before noted as much as a diesel puff coming into his air-conditioned Mercedes.

His hand fell to the armrest, and he touched all the window switches to raise any that might be down, betraying him, letting in the miasma that burned his sinuses. But all were shut and tight. He'd go the other way.

He rolled down all his windows to clear the cabin. Arkansas air blasted in at eighty-three miles per hour, ruining his hair, pulling his tie through the sunroof like a noose, sucking debris from under his seat. Deafening, hot, and moist. But it did the trick. Mostly. The smell retreated to a hint, a base note of lingering scorch in the back of his throat until he pulled into his office.

Then, it was a sound. Clicking. Distant and approaching. Irregular and omnipresent. He heard it in the parking lot and it stopped him. Still smelling the faint decay, he thought it must be his car. Maybe he'd hit something—an animal. Flesh burned by the engine, it had broken something, something was rubbing on something else. Something touching. Something... Click click click. Click click. He covered his ears, and still the sound came undiminished.

Then, the thought. Not a memory but an idea. Derrick Ecoes. A face he had not summoned in years. Events he had buried away. A dead man years past. It was like the odor and the sound —the memory of Ecoes, an unwanted sensation of unknown origin.

Susan met him at the elevator. "I was just going for bagels," she said, putting on her smile and waiting for him to notice her cleavage. "Can I get you something special?"

"No. Don't be long. I'll need you."

"Okay." He didn't even glance, and she knew he was distracted. The leering was his trademark and her job security. She put it aside and boarded the elevator.

The smell lingered in his nose, the sound in his ears, and the unbidden thought of Derrick Ecoes lurked beneath it all as he read his emails, responded to a couple, scribbled some notes, but his distraction was too much. When Susan came back with bagels, he called her in.

"Susan, call my doctor and see if I can get in right away."

"Something wrong?"

"No, I just want to catch up."

Susan left his office, stung by his curtness. She listed his cases in her mind and tried to find something that could explain his foul mood but found only the usual cases which he'd had for years. His personal life must be failing. Maybe now was her chance to step in, but she didn't like him when he was short like this—and he was often short—so she put that thought out of her mind and looked up the doctor's number.

Lamont was on the internet then, searching for new details on his old case. He found the law listings of the conviction, sentencing, appeals, and execution. Nothing new there in seven years. He studied the dates looking for anniversaries that might have come up triggering some subconscious connection that weighed on him now. Nothing.

"Kevan." Susan at the door. "Your doctor is out of town, and the office is closed until the fifth. They suggested a trip to Urgent Care if it's urgent and the emergency room if it's an emergency."

"Useless," he said.

She paused at the door, awaiting new instructions. He didn't look well. There were sweat stains under his arms, and his ears were pink. He looked... looked... He looked scared. She couldn't wrap her mind around it.

She crossed the room and stood behind him, rubbing his shoulders, finding them taut. She worked them with deft fingers, and he kept his eyes on the screen, not even acknowledging that she was there.

"Ecoes," she said. "That was an old case of yours. Something come up?"

"No... just... uhm."

"Is this bothering you?"

"What?"

"The shoulder rub?"

He flinched when he realized she was rubbing his back.

"No, it's great."

He searched on the name Jed Warner. "Whoa," he said.

Susan leaned in and read an obituary over Lamont's shoulder. "Who's Jed Warner?"

"He was, uhm... nothing. Get me Phil Brakman on the phone."

"The DA?"

"Last time I checked."

Susan left. Lamont studied the screen.

Derrick Ecoes had been executed for killing Jed Warner's two stepchildren. Ecoes swore to the final moment of his short twenty-two years that he was innocent, that he was being railroaded because he practiced magick—magick with a "k"—some version of witchcraft he was proud to talk about. This had done nothing to ingratiate him with the God-fearing jury or the folks of Hallington where he lived among strident churchgoers who didn't need more reasons to dislike him beyond his dark skin but found it in his religion. Ecoes had called his troubles—possibly quite accurately—a literal witch hunt, a line that Lamont had used in his defense and single appeal. To no avail.

"Brakman on line one."

Lamont picked up the phone. "Phil."

"Kevan, why the call?" Straight to it. Phil Brakman didn't like talking to Kevan Lamont. Their worlds had divided after the Ecoes case—Lamont's to private sleaze and paydays, his to political heights as the district attorney with his sights set on a higher office.

"Did you see that Jed Warner died last month?"

"No. So what?"

"Did anything come of the investigation into him?"

"What investigation?" said Brakman. "Ecoes went down for it. Crime solved."

"Did he ever do anything else?"

"He was executed."

"Warner?"

There was something in Lamont's voice that made Brakman turn on his computer. "I shouldn't be doing this," he said.

"There are lots of things we shouldn't do and shouldn't have done."

"That's what this is about?"

"What else."

"Old news, Kevan. Ecoes was a bad kid."

"Warner killed those girls."

"We don't know that. He had an alibi."

"Flimsy."

"And we had eyewitness testimony."

"Coerced out of a mentally impaired vagrant. 51 IQ."

"A couple of details the defense failed to bring up at the trial," said Brakman. It was blunt, but his old nemesis—or was it partner?—needed a reality check.

Lamont took a deep breath, and his head filled with stink. He gagged, coughed into the receiver.

"Take it easy, Kevan."

"Phil. Phil... We knew—"

"Ecoes was a bad kid. A true outcast. If we didn't get him, the mob would have." The word had slipped out. We. The DA was not proud of his actions in that case, the conspiracy between prosecution, defense, and cracker town fathers to put Derrick Ecoes on death row, but it was far too late to do anything about it now. The only thing that could happen now was embarrassment and wrecked careers.

"Kevan," he said. "I don't like this conversation. You getting a case of propriety? Some insurance investigator show you Kali?"

"What?"

"I'll deny everything."

"I'm not accusing. I'm not confessing," said Lamont only now sensing the threat this call contained. "Just look."

"Warner kept his nose clean," said Brakman reading the reports. "A couple speeding tickets. Had a row in Florida over a solicitation of a minor but claimed free speech and got out of it."

"A minor?" said Lamont. "That fits the earlier profile."

"What's gotten into you, Kevan?"

"I was just thinking about Ecoes, you know?"

"Magick?"

"Uhm..."

"Jesus, Kevan, you'd be the last person he'd mess with. You were all he had. Poor black trash in Arkansas. He was damn lucky to have you."

"What if he found out?"

"He didn't. He thanked you, didn't he? Some of his last words were for you, if I recall."

"What if he found out afterwards?"

"Jesus, Kevan. Grow the hell up."

"He asked for his execution to be moved up, you remember?"

"What's happening?"

"Do you remember that?"

"Yes, Kevan. I remember that."

"Do you remember why?" Lamont's eyes stung. Sweat had run into them, poured down from his forehead. The smell was back, thickening and joining the salt to his eyes. Click click click came from the phone, the window, under his desk. Ecoes' face in his mind.

"Religious reasons," said Phil Brakman.

"That's right. He said he wanted to die when stars were aligned properly for him."

"I thought it was the moon."

"All of it," said Lamont. "He explained it to me. He'd

checked charts—planned the hour and the light, the season—all so he could do something afterwards."

"Made my job easier."

"Timing. It was all about timing. He called it the witching hour. The moment when everything is conducive."

"Kevan, do I need to be worried about you? I don't want to talk about this."

Phil's voice was icy, threatening. It broke Lamont out of his spin. His ears quieted. He breathed through his mouth.

"I'm sorry, Phil. I'm fine. I'm just having a strange day."

"Kevan, sounds like you need to get some rest. Let someone else chase the next ambulance. Go fishing or something."

"Okay but—"

"But?"

"But has anything bothered you lately? Have you sensed—"

"No. I haven't thought of it in years. After I hang up, it'll be gone again. Old news. A poor black kid who no one liked turned to crime and paid the price. A cautionary tale. A blip any way you look at it."

"It jump-started your career."

"And yours," said Brakman, his patience eroding as he wondered if he'd have to do something about Lamont. "I got a reputation, you got famous. I think we both came out alright."

"Yeah."

"Get some rest. I gotta go. Don't call me again." Brakman hung up the phone.

After a moment, Lamont called his secretary. "Dee, don't log that last call."

He put the phone down and stared at his receiver for a long moment waiting in vain for the clicking to stop, the odor to leave, his head to settle.

Then, it was a taste.

Bitter and hot. Pepper, lemon, garlic. Mud and sand. Copper and coal. Raspy and thick. He gagged at it, felt his tongue thicken for it, his mouth go dry.

He reached for his coffee and swished it, burned his mouth, his cheeks, his tongue. He gargled it just the same and swallowed. Another sip filled his mouth, and he held it, a liquid bandage, hot and bitter.

He looked up the nearest Urgent Care.

Swallow. Rush of filth. Coughing.

"Susan, I'm going to get checked out. For a lark, could you follow up on Jed Warner?"

"You sense a wrongful death?"

"Get the details. Look for anything weird."

He scraped his tongue on his teeth and left Susan at her desk.

Susan looked through the appointment book and saw that Lamont was going to miss several meetings. She began making phone calls to reschedule them, making excuses that wouldn't alarm the clients or make her employer look lazy or weak. While she phoned, she ran searches on Jed Warner.

Before she had finished her last call, she'd found the connection between Kevan Lamont and the late Jed Warner through the Derrik Ecoes case. Warner had been floated as the real killer, at least in some media accounts. Lamont had never brought up the possibility, at least not anywhere she could see. The accusations had been made by neighbors and civil rights groups, none of whom were ever called by the defense.

His passing had been ruled "death by misadventure." He'd fallen down a flight of stairs and broken his neck. His windpipe was crushed and pressed against the last step. Unable to move, he'd choked to death. She tried to find any hint of negligence, but the building was federal, a Social Security office no less, meticulously compliant. She found a report from an employee who said Warner appeared to be sick, coughing, spitting on the floor. Flinching at sudden sounds.

She saw no case here. He was a nobody with a checkered past. As for timing, the only thing she noticed, and this not something she'd ever share with Kevan Lamont because it was her hobby and none too professional, was that when he'd died, the stars had been in dark alignment and the moon full. Just like tonight.

Lamont made one stop at the pharmacy before going home. He texted Susan to reschedule the rest of his day and wasn't surprised to find she had already done it. While he waited for his prescription, he sucked menthol cough drops and restarted his smoking habit, chaining Lucky Strikes in the parking lot, remembering—against his will—the determined face of Derrick Ecoes as he sat in the chair, eyes closed, lips moving around the bit in his gagged mouth.

Though lethal injection was the norm, Alabama allowed the convicted to choose electrocution as an alternative. Ecoes had chosen that, saying he'd use the energy to get things done. He was talking like that at the end, like a born-again mystic, a martyr for a cause he couldn't name. Lamont wouldn't say that his client had been happy to die, but he'd faced it with a confidence he'd not seen before. It was more than calm resignation; it was purpose, as if he were setting out on a task. At least that's how Kevan Lamont saw it now.

He collected the pills, took two dry, and drove home with a cigarette burning in his mouth, the music turned to blasting, his speed illegal and dangerous. He didn't know why he was rushing, but the movement felt good, forced him to concentrate on the road, and kept Ecoes out of his head. The pills were giving him a touch of euphoria, and he remembered why he'd liked them so much before rehab.

Back at home, dusk, Lamont staggered into the house, closing the garage behind him. At the kitchen sink, he splashed cold water on his face, drenching his shirt collar and threatening his silk tie.

Dusk. He'd wasted a day waiting for a prescription, and before that, a doctor who told him nothing. A migraine. "We'll know more after the blood work." Did he suggest a scan of some kind? Someone mentioned it. Hadn't they?

Lie down in a dark room.

He peeled off his suit in his bedroom, chewing another cough drop. The sound of hard candy against his teeth filled his head with noise, taste his mouth, and heavy menthol his nose.

Then, it was vision.

It could have startled the hell out of him. It should have, but his brain was on the fritz, and when he saw Derrik Ecoes in the mirror standing behind him, he took it as par for the course. He closed his eyes, ran more water, and splashed it until his hair was drenched and dripping. He wet a towel, took another pill.

When he looked again, Ecoes was still there, a blurry shadow in a misted mirror. Lamont could see his black face over his white tee-shirt, but his eyes lost in the gloom.

When Lamont turned around and the figure didn't move, he pulled up and paused.

His senses were rattled, the nod coming on from the opiates. He ripped his mind back from wherever it had been and stared at the apparition, willing it to leave with a willpower born of incredulity, unreality, and denial. Fierce and fighting, he stared it down until the form moved backward and out of the room into the hall, where it faded. Fading. Fading. Gone.

"You don't know," Lamont said. "You didn't then. You couldn't now."

When the lights were off and the curtains pulled tight, he laid on his bed with the cool, damp cloth over his eyes.

"More of migraine and mustard than grave about you," he said aloud and smiled at his wit.

He took a deep breath and smelled clear filtered air. Swallowed and tasted nothing but spit. Listened, and all was quiet. He was blind behind the cloth. Stillness in his mind.

A sudden migraine. Too much stress. Forgotten guilt resurfacing from a weakened condition. Misfiring synapses all.

He drifted toward sleep, riding the wave of the drug, imagining pools of cool water, sun-drenched beaches on the Gulf, new conquests in bikinis able to be had for the cost of a margarita.

Coconut oil and shrimp, waves crashing in the distance. Pleasant thrum. Calm and soothing.

He woke himself with his own coughing, rolling over in his bed gasping for breath. The air was sour and burnt, his tongue tasted of iron and rot, his ears brought him the throbbing loud as a trumpet. In the dark, his eyes flashed with light, tracers in the blackness.

He knocked over his clock and wallet, phone and pill bottle, to turn on the lamp. The room filled with an orange glow from beneath a tangerine lampshade, showing him he was home, in his bed, but showing him also the figure of Derrick Ecoes standing over him. The ghost stared down with unblinking eyes, bloodshot and piercing, the same expression of purpose he'd worn when the switch clicked over and he was electrocuted to death.

Click in his ears, his memory of the moment.

Burned and dead. Mucus running down his dead lips. Slobber from his mouth.

Lamont pulled away. Tangled in his bedding, he rolled to the other side.

There was Ecoes too.

Back the other way. Lamont fell onto the floor among his nightstand detritus, under the unearthly light, sheets tangled around him.

He reached for the pill bottle, anxious to get another, to deaden himself before—

The bottle was empty.

Like a remembered movie, he saw himself wake and take a pill. The scene in loop. Roll over, take pill. Repeat repeat. Repeat.

Above him, Ecoes, barefoot, jeans cut to the knees, scorch marks on his ankles, his white shirt blackened from its burning. The smell of singed hair. The taste of death. The click of the switch killing an innocent man.

Standing but a handbreadth away, Ecoes stared down at Kevan, silently watching him with tortured, bloodshot, unblinking eyes, his face that same damned expression of purpose.

Lamont threw himself to the window above his bed. He ripped at the curtains, pulled them from the rod, the hardware from the wall. He winced at the brightness. White moonlight filled the room as the distant orb joined Ecoes in his vigil, watching coldly from its height.

Lamont fell back and screamed. His body was heavy, his mind a blur. He thought of all the pills he'd taken, or thought he'd taken, and wondered how he was still alive, how he had any sensation at all. He should have long since slid into an opium dream, long since gone numb, long since gone coma. Senseless long before he could have ever finished the bottle taking them one at a time like that. He marveled that he could think or smell, taste, hear or see, after such a—

And then like a jolt of malignant, painful lightning, he felt it.

———————

A month after Lamont's overdose, Phil Brakman brushed his teeth in the mirror of his mistress's bathroom. He admired his new haircut, planning what he'd say to the lieutenant governor that day when he first noticed the smell.

Deafening
M.H. LOPEZ

Your mouth was
a tectonic plate
Drifting away from
the last words
that you spoke to me
s e p a r a t e d

like crisscrossing drifters
under a Blue Moon
moving through
costal opaque cobalt

blue on the
Starlight
Railroad
lost in the sides of
the Sierra Nevada Mountains
buried at midnight
in the abyss of the Pacific

Joel

CLAUDENE B. GORDON

After a few months separation from teaching school, I was delighted to teach a Sunday School class. I was given a group of ten mischievous ten year old boys. *Once a teacher, always a teacher,* I thought. I've got this!

What an awakening! Teaching school and church instruction have few similarities. I found there was no principal's office to send a misbehaving youth, and my only control was a bribe of cookies at the end of class, contingent upon good behavior.

The first week I dramatized "David and Goliath" with proper voice inflections for each character and expressive words. But while Biblical David bent to retrieve a smooth stone for his slingshot, present day Joel tipped over his chair and faked banging his head against the wall. In mock pain, he began a wild uproar, and a couple of the other boys tried the same stunt. This broke the entire class into pandemonium, and by the time peace was restored, Goliath was still standing.

I tried every teaching trick I could think of the next three weeks, but each class erupted into trouble. The best prank was sliding piecemeal out the window—you know, first an arm, then a leg---and out! Several followed.

Spitballs came next, sticking on the ceiling, and secret hands signals passed among them. In desperation I called for help. The Sunday School president visited my class and agreed we needed parental support. Together, we visited each boy's home and met with him and his parents. The next Sunday, we were amazed at the somber group that greeted us—except for Joel.

It became evident that the class problems were mostly initiated by Joel as he was unaffected by our home visit. All by himself he continued disrupting the class. I begged, cajoled and bribed him, but to no avail. My patience diminished. I began to hope that he'd be absent, maybe develop the flu. But of all the boys, he was 100% attender. He loved coming!

During the week that followed, I pieced together a personality profile of Joel: a middle child of a large family, a lonely boy and failing in school. Compassion softened my heart, but I firmly concluded I could not reach him.

"Dear Lord," I prayed. "Is it possible that I have been placed in the wrong vineyard?"

I found I was bracing myself before each class period, reminding myself it was only for an hour. But then came the Sunday which will remain imprinted on my mind.

It was raining—raining so hard that each boy entered the primary room dripping wet. As the opening prayer was being said, a commotion began at the end of our row. I kept my eyes closed as I heard various comments getting closer to me.

"Ouch! Get off my toes!"

"Yuck! You stink!"

"No, you can't sit by me!"

I opened my eyes and saw Joel push the smaller boy next to me aside with a rough shove and plop himself, mud splashed and sticky, by my side. He smelled like a wet dog. A revolting feeling overpowered me.

At that moment, the clouds suddenly broke and a beam of light shone through the church window upon a painting at the front of the chapel. This caught Joel's attention and with unusual urgency he grabbed my arm.

"Teacher! Teacher! Look!"

My eyes followed his pointing finger to a picture I only casually noticed earlier. It was a large oil painting of Jesus sitting on a grassy knoll in streaming white robes. Around him stood a group of several beautiful children, all focused with loving eyes upon the Savior.

Jesus seemed to be looking directly at one of them, a small boy whose body leaned forward upon a forked wooden crutch. The Savior was reaching a caring hand toward this child, His eyes reflecting unconditional love and compassion.

Joel continued. "Teacher, that boy, the one with a crutch, that's me! That's me!"

"What do you mean that's you?" He had my full attention now.

"When the artist was painting that picture he needed a model for the boy with a crutch. The artist asked me to act like I was that boy while he painted me. That's really a painting of me up there with Jesus!"

All at once the sunlight seemed to brighten my entire soul. A lump rose in my throat while tears misted my eyes. Now I could really see! The message from Him in that very scene seemed to burn in my heart.

"Suffer little children to come unto me and forbid them not." He seemed to be speaking to me saying 'I love Joel just the way he is. He needs acceptance, attention. You can love him too.'

I felt a warmth flow through me, calming my distress and

replacing annoyance with peaceful feelings. Maybe it was forgiveness for a confused, hurting young boy. I knew it was balm for my injured soul. All Joel wanted was for me to love him. Of all the teaching skills and methods I used, I forgot that "love never faileth."

I slipped my arm softly around Joel's stiff shoulders as he snuggled into my embrace. My tears joined with the rain in his wet hair. He turned his smiling face up to me, reflecting a sweet innocence with, for sure, just a hint of mischief.

The Barber of Boot Hill
BRYAN YOUNG

"You a dentist?" the cowboy with piercing blue eyes asked as he stepped up the wooden steps to my humble shop.

"I'm a barber," I told him, but that didn't mean anything to him or his companion, a cowboy with a rust-colored mustache and hair to match. The red-headed fella's jaw swelled on one side, and he held it tight as though that'd do anything for the pain. I coulda been the King of Siam for all he cared as long as I could fix his aching tooth.

"Well, surely you do some fixin' up of people now and again," the blue-eyed cowboy said, pointing to the front of my shop. "Leastways, that's what your pole says."

He was right. I had all the stripes for fixing cuts and bandaging people up, but with Doc Calloway in town, the need for me to do that sort of thing had dried up like the river. "Doc Calloway's place is just up on the hill, and I think he'd be more than happy to oblige you fellas if you went up that way. He's a mite better at that sort of thing than I am."

The blue-eyed cowboy who did the talking smiled broadly.

He seemed a likable sort. "I mean, we're short on time and it's just a simple extraction I'd bet. You understand, right?"

The man with the toothache moaned as they backed me further toward the entrance to my barbershop.

"We'll make it worth your while..."

And while that was a nice enough gesture, I figured I'd've helped the poor fella anyway, because that's just the sort I am. Generous to a fault and kind as a kitten. I nodded my head back to the open door and sighed. "Fine. Come on in."

I turned and went in, proud of the shop I'd built. Two chairs meant I could leave a fella with a hot towel on one while I shaved another. A polished tin mirror ran along one wall, and the sunlight, especially in the morning like now, poured into the place like honey. The wooden floors and walls soaked it up with a gleam.

A shelf with all my instruments sat beneath the oil lamps, and thin strips of horse hide dangled from the shelf and each chair. "Why don't you have your friend take a seat just there," I said, pointing to the seat at the back.

If this fella's tooth spurted a lot of blood, that seat was closest to the water pump in the back where the tubs were.

"Nice place you got here," the blue-eyed cowboy said, waving his hat across the shop as he regarded it.

"Many thanks, stranger. I do my best."

"It's the sort of place that makes a fella *want* to come and bathe."

"That's the idea."

The stricken cowboy in the denim jacket ambled toward the chair and then collapsed into it like he couldn't support his weight any longer. I hadn't dealt with a tooth that painful in a long time. Teeth were never my specialty, but I knew my way around the grip of a pair of pliers.

I left the cowboys in the front room while I went to collect my tools from the back. I put the pliers, a smattering of cotton, and the ether and rag in the front of my apron and searched for my oldest cape. No sense in getting blood on the nicest one.

"It's fine," the talker said quietly. Maybe he figured I couldn't hear. "We'll get it taken care of, lickety split. Then we'll make the opening, no problem."

The patient groaned. Maybe there were words in there, but I couldn't make 'em out.

"No, you'll be fine. Good as new. This is gonna go easy as anything." The cowboy's voice was as smooth as my shave and well-oiled, like he'd be able to talk anybody into anything. I figured that's why they wore irons on their hips. He'd've had to butter the sheriff up like a Christmas goose to get into town without having to surrender their pieces.

That or they were up to something nefarious.

The one in the chair said something that sounded a lot like incredulity.

"Have I ever led you wrong?"

Was that a laugh of sarcasm through the pain?

I came back into the room. My boots clicked sharp against the wood, announcing my return.

"So, it'll be a dollar and a half for the extraction," I said, spreading the cape over the ailing gentleman and the six-shooter sitting in his lap. His eyes widened a bit when he saw me eyeing it, but I didn't mention it. "Least, a dollar-fifty is what I charged when I used to do it often."

"That's a fair price," the cowboy said, clapping his hands in front of him.

I felt a "but" coming on.

And I was right.

"But," he said, "to tell the truth, he and I ain't gotta penny to rub together between us at the moment."

"I see," I said, finishing up the knot in the cape at the back of the fella's neck.

"But I'll tell ya what," the cowboy said, rubbing his hands together. "We're fixin' to make some real money today, and we'll make you whole. Ya just have to take my word for it."

I narrowed my eyes at the cowboy, skeptical.

He raised a hand up like he was swearin' on a bible. "On my honor. We wouldn't take a thing like this lightly. And like I said, you'd get your due and proper. You'd just need to fix him up and let us get it first."

"You gotta job in town?" I asked.

"Somethin' like that. But he can't do it with that damned toothache of his. It's just too bad." The cowboy fished a watch on a chain from his pocket, checked the time, and tsked. "And we're just running low on time is all."

I debated in my mind. I looked from the fella in the chair to the fella doin' the talking, back and forth, searchin' for an answer. But the look of agony on the poor guy's face, the swell of his cheek, and the moans he issued were enough to sway my heart. If I've said it before, I'll say it again: I'm generous to a fault and kind as a kitten.

I didn't take an oath like any sort of doctor, but when a person comes to you in pain, you do your best to fix 'em up. It's just the human thing to do, ain't it? "All right. But you'll oblige me by fillin' out an IOU, if that meets your approval."

"More than happy, more than happy. It'll only be a formality, though, because you'll be getting your money, plus a little bonus, today."

An extra nickel on the fee would have been enough to make me happy.

"If you want to get to work on him," the fella said, walking over to the counter at the front of my shop, "I'll draft up an IOU."

"There's a ledger with paper in the top drawer, a pencil, too," I told him.

He went to work on the proper paperwork while I stood over his distressed friend, readying a rag for the ether.

"No, no ether," he said from the other side of the room.

"What?"

"No, he, uh, he doesn't react well to it."

I couldn't even imagine the pain he'd be in if'n I yanked that son of a bitch tooth without anything to put him at ease against the pain. Even just the thought of feeling the pliers on tooth enamel without the juice was enough to make me cringe.

I looked down to the patient, and his wide and frightened eyes told me everything I needed to know.

If I hadn't've been able to figure it on my own, his growling, lock-jawed pleas woulda filled me in. "Ether..." he said from one side of his mouth.

But the smooth-talker came over, smiling like anything, hand raised toward his friend. "Now, you know we've got to do this job, and you're not gonna be able if you're stumbling around like a jackass on ether. I need you sharp."

The man in the chair refused to make eye contact with his friend. His eyes watered just a bit as he clenched his jaw and put pressure on the offending tooth.

"He says he wants the ether," I said, going back to dousing the rag.

"No, we can't do that." He pulled his watch again, then he dangled the face in the direction of his friend. "I'm sorry, but we're outta time. If you wanna get this done beforehand, you're gonna have to do it now. No ether, nothin'."

The poor bastard shook his head.

"Listen, mister," I told his friend. "He wants the ether."

"Wantin' ain't havin', and he knows he can't."

The man in the chair closed his eyes as his friend got closer.

"Listen, you know we've got work to do. And I wouldn't ask you to do this if we didn't. But you're the one who needed this, and I didn't balk. I said it would be a bad idea and we should wait, but you said it hurt too bad. Now I told you if you wanted the ether, we could wait, but you're the one who said you couldn't. So do you want to let the man do his work and we'll be on our way or not?"

The fella in the chair growled like a whining pup, and I couldn't blame him with the way his jaw was swelled. It looked ready to pop. I hadn't even got a look at the tooth yet, and I knew it was a monster.

"Efff…" was the noise he made.

"What was that?" his friend asked, holding his hand to his ear.

"FFuhhh…" he said this time.

The fella in the chair took a breath in and clenched again to speak, tears streamin' down his face. "I said… fine…"

"See? Now he's talkin' sense." The cowboy looked to me with a smile. "So you just get in there and pull that damn thing out and we'll be on our way, and you'll be a mite richer soon as can be."

I furrowed my brow. "Well, all right. If that's the way you both want it."

It didn't make too much difference to me. Sure, he'd be a bit more still on the ether, but it was more for him than anybody.

The man in the chair rolled his eyes and braced himself, gripping the arms with white knuckles like he was dangling from a roof.

"You ready then?"

He nodded his head and kept his eyes shut.

I stuffed the bottle of ether back into my apron pocket and withdrew the pliers. They were a sturdy pair and would do the trick fast, which is exactly what he needed.

He didn't need to see anything, and I told him so. I tried calming him as best I could, but I don't know how anyone in their right mind coulda stayed calm knowing what was about to happen.

"You need a drink?"

He nodded his head profusely, so I went to the counter and fixed him a slug of whiskey and brought it back fast. He sipped at it through his clenched teeth, and the brown liquid dripped down his stubbled chin.

"Take it all in," I told him, and he did. He handed the glass back, and I placed it on the shelf in front of the mirror.

"I'm gonna need you to open up now, stranger."

He parted his lips but left his jaw tightened. I knew that feeling. The one where you're puttin' pressure on the pain, and the second that pressure leaves, you just feel like the pain is gonna be so bad that you're gonna float away in a balloon and want to just jump because it hurts so damn bad. That's why he didn't want to let go of the grip he had on that tooth.

"I know it hurts, but I'm gonna need to get you to open a little wider than that. I need to see the tooth afore I can take it out."

He grumbled some as his teeth parted, but there on the bottom I could see the swell around one of the molars, half black with rot. It needed to come out something fierce, and no part of it was gonna feel good. "Yeah, that one looks like it's been treatin' you like a son of a bitch for a while, hasn't it?"

He squeaked with pain but couldn't make a more intelligible

sound. He nodded his head though, which told me I had the long and the short of it.

"Now, I'm gonna put this in your mouth, I'm gonna grip it tight, and I'm gonna pull like hell. It's gonna hurt, you get me? Like, more than anything you've ever felt. You been shot?"

The fella in the chair shrugged and shook his head tightly again. He'd definitely been shot.

"It's gonna feel like that. But the difference is this gets better pretty instantly. You're gonna be sore, but not like you are now. And by tomorrow or the day after, you'll be grateful you came. Now, are you ready?"

He shook his head and closed his eyes, opening his mouth even wider.

"Good, just like that," I told him.

Turning the pliers over, I eased them into his mouth, eyeing carefully the spot I needed to clamp. I didn't want to tighten the pliers down on it until the last possible second, and I wanted to give him as much warning as I could. Even just touching the thing was going to hurt, and I didn't want him squirreling beneath me. If he was to buck the wrong way, it'd cause us both a lotta hurt.

"You ready? I'm gonna do it now. You're gonna have to keep still for both our sakes, else this is gonna hurt a lot worse. You get me?"

He closed his eyes tighter and gripped the armrests of the chair like they were the only path to holy salvation.

"Here we go, fella."

I crunched the pliers down on the tooth. Even through the handle, I felt the grit and heard the crunch against what little enamel there was left.

I counted as I slowly added pressure to my grip.

"One," I told him, the pliers tightening in my hand.

"Two," I said, squeezing harder.

The poor fella's eyes leaked through his shut lids, and his fingers looked like they might break they gripped the chair so tight.

"Three."

I wrenched the tooth out.

Blood dripped from it against the white cape.

I never quite get used to the delayed reaction of the scream. The blood went from his face, and the poor bastard took on a cadaverous pallor like he'd lost a gallon of blood rather than just a tooth. His hands shot to his mouth and held it. But even then, the swelling was already going down in his face.

"See?" his buddy said. "I told you that wouldn't be so bad. You're all fixed up now, and we'll, uh, we'll just be on our way."

I looked at the tooth held tight in the end of the mouth of the pliers, dripping blood. "He might need a minute."

The talkative one plucked his watch from his pocket again and tapped on the face. "Well, a minute is something he doesn't have. Thanks again, Doc."

I untied the bloody cape from his neck and uncovered him, but he made no move to stand. Not until his friend came over and helped him to his feet and got his gun back in its holster.

"I told you you'd get through that just fine," his friend said. "That was a helluva thing. Never seen anything like it. You took it like a champion."

The cowboy with the blue eyes turned to me as his buddy shuffled to the door. "I knew you'd come through for us. Thanks for that. And I promise you'll get what's coming to you."

"He'll need this," I said, pulling the fluff of cotton from my apron.

"Oh, right."

The poor fella turned to me and took the cotton.

"You'll want to pack it in tight and let it soak in the blood. Don't want to swallow too much. Until it stops bleeding, anyway."

He braced himself, closed his eyes, and stuffed the cotton in his bloodied mouth.

"Much obliged," he said, his words muffled through the anguish and the cotton.

They left as fast as they came, and I wondered what it was they were doing to earn their money. I didn't think too hard about it. I went about cleaning up the shop. I dropped the tooth in a tin and washed the pliers in one of the tubs and returned it to the shelf.

The gunshots were distant, from the other side of main street. When the firing got closer, I went for the shotgun under the counter. I didn't know what the trouble was, but I had a guess. Being caught unawares would have been a damn foolish thing, and the last thing I wanted to be was a damn fool.

The shooting stopped, and I heard a whole pile of shouting. A horse whinnied. People were running. The sheriff barked some orders, and I gripped my shotgun even tighter.

Creeping up to the front window, I snuck a peek. Dust kicked up from the firefight, and gun smoke filled the street. The scent of black powder hit me, and I knew it had gotten too close for comfort.

That's when the back door creaked open.

"Who's that?" I shouted.

Leapin' to my feet, I hightailed it to the back just in time to see the door close again.

"Hello?"

But there was no one to be seen. I aimed the shotgun at each tub, wondering if somebody coulda been hiding in one of them, but both were empty.

"Anybody?"

Somebody had to have opened the door.

And that's when I noticed it, sitting in front of the back door.

A big rock holdin' down some paper.

It looked like a page from my ledger.

Walking over, I kicked the rock over with my boot. It *was* a page from my ledger. Bending down, I lifted the paper, and seein' what it was shocked me to my core.

The IOU.

And beneath it, two crisp ten dollar bills.

I turned the IOU over to find a note written on the back. "Couldn't have done it without ya –Butch."

"Well, I'll be a damned fool."

Twilight Walk

MARIE TOLLSTRUP

Lighted windows at twilight bar me from cozy worlds
behind lemon-paned glass. The fall chill snakes,
coiling my neck, and cold slithers to my toes. My
heart drops to shriveled leaves, and boots' crunch
sends shivers up my outsider-spine. Lighted windows
at twilight—their glow an invitation to enter. I yearn
for light's embrace, to burst in like wind gusts that
pummel me on solo walks.

I swallow bitter isolation. My heart's aflutter to know
lives nestled behind radiant windows, protected the
way wallpaper disguises flaws. Lighted windows at
twilight swim into my darkening world. On blustery
streets, I press forward, light, a beacon leading to my
door. My breathing quickens, and I sprint in rhythmic
lunge. Window's gleam, a torch that sets my world
awash in light, banishes cold haunting solitude.

Her Voice

DAVID RODEBACK

There's nothing like the sound of a mom reading to her children, when they're your children too. It's the exact opposite of their nightmares, the universal antidote to whatever imagined horrors the darkness may conceal. It works on me too, easing me away from today's and tomorrow's cares. And everything sounds better in Ann's British accent.

"*The Tale of Peter Rabbit*, by Beatrix Potter. Read by Mum, for Jake and Amber.

"Once upon a time, there were four little Rabbits, and their names were…"

Jake and Amber are still young enough to enjoy snuggling in our bed for their bedtime stories, and they're small enough to fit there between Ann and me. I'm in my pajamas because my bedtime is early too; I have to be on station by 5:00 a.m., almost an hour away. On work nights I hardly ever hear the end of the first story. I love falling asleep to Ann's voice.

When it's not a work night, I'm there for stories anyway. I love staying awake to her voice.

Sometimes in the middle of the night, half-awake for a fleeting moment, I'll put my arm around the warm body beside me, and she'll snuggle against me in her sleep and purr. At 3:45 a.m., when it's time for me to get up, I try not to wake her, but she drowsily welcomes and sometimes returns a hug and kiss before falling back into sleep for a couple more hours.

I shower, dress, and pause for a moment in each child's doorway, gazing happily on small, quietly slumbering forms in the pale white glow of the moon. Then it's off to work.

That's how things are for me at home, how they're supposed to be. I'm not content with everything in my life, and I don't always love a routine, but I love this one.

That is, I loved it until the storm came.

This morning, it's harder to wake up than it used to be, and it takes longer. Even as I fumble for my phone to turn off the alarm, I'm not certain I'm awake.

The moon's up, shining faintly through the bedroom window, but the color's wrong—brown, yellow, weak, eerie. The light is like sludge; it should probably smell bad. The alarm's cruel beeping is off a bit too. I must be more tired than usual, or maybe I'm coming down with something. I turn it off before it wakes Ann.

I roll over to put my arm around her and give her a squeeze and a kiss.

My arm falls onto the cool sheet. The wrongness of that shocks me fully awake.

The sheet feels crisp and clean on her side of the bed. No one has slept there since laundry day, at least.

Her walk-in closet is next to my not-walk-in closet. I quietly open its doors, because I love that it smells like her. This morning, it just smells like dust and smoke.

The air in the rest of the house smells like smoke too. It seems like that's not new, but it hasn't always been that way.

Just past the closets is the master bathroom. The moonlight's wrong there too, and flipping the light switch doesn't help as much as I expect. The face in the mirror is off—my own, almost, but there's something hollow about the eyes, and more gray in my hair than I remember.

For all the strangeness, routine is routine. I stop at each child's doorway. By the faint yellow-brown glow I see empty, carefully made beds in unnaturally tidy rooms.

I grab my lunch from the fridge, wondering if it will taste like smoke. The brown paper bag is unusually soft, and it doesn't crinkle like a paper bag should. At first its proportions seem too wide and too short, and its angles are odd, but I blink a couple of times and it looks normal.

It's time to leave.

Our home sits on the outskirts of town, near the base of a mountain and the edge of a forest. I have countless memories of watching the sun rise into a clear blue sky above evergreens and gray peaks, while ten thousand birds chirp and sing, and our whole world smells of pine, aspen, and scrub oak.

Now, in the smoky silence, those memories feel distant and unreal. The sounds of my truck's door closing and its engine starting are unnaturally loud.

My office is a Forest Service watchtower, thirteen miles in. The last ten miles are a primitive track that makes my four-wheel-drive Toyota a necessity, not a toy.

This morning, after the first mile, I see no other lights at all—not on the road or off, not on land or in the sky. The moon's gone, and I cannot see the countless stars. If I could, they'd be a lush blanket of lights such as no one ever sees in the city.

My burly Tundra is the only light source in this world. Its headlights make the surrounding darkness darker.

The forest should be full of wildlife, but after the second mile I see no animal, large or small. The reason's in my headlights, when they shine on what used to be aspens. Now they're naked trunks, forlorn shadows on the mountainsides, mostly black, with uncharred streaks of whitish bark.

The fire here was recent enough, but I never saw the flames, and I barely remember the smoke. The night shift watchman called it in. He saw the lightning bolt that started it, about the time I emerged from the mountains after my shift and noticed all the flashing lights on the freeway, a mile and a half away.

The storm brought mostly wind and lightning to the mountains, but there were sudden, heavy downpours in the valley. On the watery freeway five lives ended quickly in a multi-vehicle crash. Three of them were mine.

It wasn't Ann's fault, said the state troopers at the front door. She hadn't caused it. It was just bad luck. An accident. Nothing Anyone Could Do.

Everyone was so very, very sorry for my loss.

The fire in the forest was out, by the time I returned to work, many days later.

Fog shrouds the road ahead, but when I reach it, it's dull and brownish, not reflective and white. I know it's smoke from 300 miles upwind, not from the forest I watch for fire, but the drive into smoky blackness is too familiar. I feel as if I should be accustomed to this nightmare, but I'm not.

How would one become accustomed to this?

I work alone, a 12-hour shift. Ty is nearly always there as I arrive, ending his own shift, but this morning there's just a note in his familiar scrawl. "Repeater down again. I'll reset it on the way home. Leaving early." The note itself is strange. I seem to remember him spelling *repeater* with all *e*'s and no *a*, and putting two *s*'s in *reset*. This morning, everything's right, and that's wrong.

Until he resets the repeater, I'm isolated. But it shouldn't be long. He lives on the other side of the mountains, a seventeen-mile drive from our post. The repeater sits just off the road and resets in two or three minutes.

In any case the rules are clear: even if communication fails, I stay at my post, except to report a fire.

When the sun climbs halfheartedly through the secondhand smoke, it's clear that only the firebreak saved the watchtower itself when the forest burned. From the far edge of the cleared area to the jagged horizon, in every direction, I see a black, lifeless dreamscape, with practically nothing left to burn.

Yet still we watch for fire.

This must be what hell is like. Alone, the smoke, the stench of charred forest, the meaningless drudgery, the silence.

I often stream music while I watch the horizon, but our internet connection depends on the same repeater. So I turn on the AM radio instead. Nothing happens, not even static. Fresh batteries don't help.

I could push back the silence by talking or singing, but I don't try. It would simply wait nearby for me to stop, and then it would return.

The repeater doesn't go back on line. No doubt, Ty will explain when he arrives for his shift, but that's hours away. In the meantime I doze. I dream of the same wasteland I see with waking eyes. It feels like a nightmare that has always been and will always be.

At noon I study my lunch bag. It's just a brown paper bag, used and reused until it's soft and verges on disintegration. I probably have new ones at home. Ann would know where.

Ty doesn't arrive for his 5:00 p.m. shift. It's been months since that happened. The rule says I'm to remain on station for an hour. Then, if he's still not here, I can leave and report.

I wait the extra hour, then two more. By then it's dark, and my drive home is through the same brown, black, smoky nightmare as my morning commute. The last two miles of forest are green and alive, but shrouded like the rest.

As I approach the valley, my phone finds a connection and vibrates with alerts. As soon as I'm home, I start with my voice mail. There are two messages from Ty. The repeater wouldn't reset, the power supply's fried, that was the spare, and a new one won't arrive until next week. Also his truck wouldn't start, so he'll be three or four hours late for his shift. But he'll be there. I text him, thanking him and wishing him luck.

Dinner is something from a can. Then I make tomorrow's lunch. I find more lunch bags in a cupboard, but they're worn soft too, so I use the one I used today. Showering washes the stench of burnt wood off me. Too bad I can't wash the air. Every light I see from my window is a dingy yellow.

At 8:30 p.m. I put on my pajamas and settle into bed. I used to pray at both ends of the day, but no more.

With the thoughtless efficiency of long habit, I tell Siri to set my phone alarm for 3:45 a.m. Then I give the last voice command of the night: "Play Ann Czerny."

Her words and voice are my refuge. Her accent is music.

"*The Tale of Peter Rabbit*, by Beatrix Potter. Read by Mum, for Jake and Amber."

She planned so carefully for her month-long trip home to Yorkshire, to help her father care for her mother after surgery. She wanted to take the children with her, but we couldn't make it work. So for the month before she left, to help them miss her a little less, she would record one story a day, every day they were in school. Twenty stories in all.

She recorded only one. Then the storm came, and she left for a different destination, and they went with her after all.

"Once upon a time, there were four little Rabbits, and their names were—"

If I'm lucky—I often am—I'll dream of her in bed beside me, with our children between us at first and then not. Of waking up early and giving her a hug and kiss, and standing in the children's doorways for a long moment, watching them sleep. And going to work in a lush mountain forest that teems with life.

12

A Genderqueer Follower of Christ: Reconciling My Religion With the Way I Feel Inside

KAM HADLEY

The Church of Jesus Christ of Latter-Day Saints teaches that we lived before we were born. In this spirit world, we had gender. It is not just something we were assigned at birth but part of who we are. (*The Family: A Proclamation to the World*)

Our physical bodies, though, create a challenge. In fact, we were sent here to this Earth *to* gain bodies and be tested. (Abraham 3:23-28) Trials are as diverse as people themselves. Each of us has hard things. Feelings are real and valid. It is not easy. It was never meant to be easy. Life is a test, after all.

For some, including myself, these physical challenges include hormone problems and male/female energy fluctuations. I don't know what all it entails, but it does affect the way I feel. It may not be visible from the outside, and it may not be part of the spirit I was before birth, but the feelings are still there, and they are real.

Being cisgender isn't *just* if you identify as the gender you were born as, but if you *feel* like the gender you were born as and identify as such. (Symptoms of Being Human by Jeff Garvin)

I don't know that I will ever be able to claim to be cisgender. My pronouns may be she/her, but I don't always *feel* she/her. This is part of who I am. It is part of the challenge of my mortal existence.

I believe my spirit is a female spirit, that I did have gender before I was born. I just believe our physical bodies, meant to test and try us, throw things for a loop. My issues may be caused by a chemical imbalance or something else, but knowing that doesn't make the way I feel less real.

So, yes, I am nonbinary. (This term means I don't feel like I fit into the boxes designated as male/female.) Yes, I am genderqueer. (This term means I struggle with my own gender identity.) Yes, I may feel more ze/zir than she/her. I am still that same female spirit as before I was born. Those other things are an expression of how I *feel*. It is me accepting one of the challenges I've been given in this life and dealing with it the best way I know how. It doesn't go away if it's shoved down and buried. It is part of me.

I am a genderqueer member of the Church of Jesus Christ of Latter-day Saints. My gender issues strengthen my testimony of the purpose of this life as a test and give me more reason to *have* to rely on my Savior, Jesus Christ, to make it through.

God, the Father of our Spirits, loves us. He wants us to come back to Him after we are done fumbling through this life. He has given us a Savior, Jesus Christ. He has descended below all we can suffer and feel. We *must* lean on Him and allow Him to buoy us up. I know without Him, I would be sunk in more ways than one.

I praise God for the matchless gift of His Divine Son. With His help and example, I take up my own cross of gender issues and keep going, even stronger than before, because I've *had* to rely on the Savior.

13

Dear Dora,

CHERIE BUTLER

Thank you for producing my best friend
Thank you for deep breathing and panting
Life into my Autumn Baby
Fall was what we did in love
Sometimes he says sent from above, other times, "It's
    fate"
I'm not irate at the fact that this gap
Feels like it stretches farther than those
Polyester pants I'm sure he wore "in the day"
He grew into that moustache that he was
Never so sure made him look mature
Dear Dora...Thank you for instilling precious
Qualities such as love, kindness, consideration and
    patience
Into that man
If I can, If I may...I must say, he's a good one
I tried to run away a thousand times, but you know what?

He's fast. Creeps up on you real slow, and before you
    know it,
The race is over. He won my heart
Dear Dora, I love his smile
I'm not sure which side of the aisle it hails from,
But it's so sincere. It's beautiful. Charming, almost
    alarming
Because you rarely see it.
I've unlocked the key to tap into what it takes for him to
Light up a room so wonderfully
He constantly amazes me...
Dear Dora, I love you even though we've never met
I bet you were as stubborn as he is
Ok, I won't talk bad about his mama...
Dear Dora, He's cried tears for you
I've felt your heartbeat through and through
He misses you, as grown as he is, he still needs you
There are words to his sentences that only you can finish
Please complete what's undone
Your son is in need of THAT woman
He's done swimming in deep waters
Trying to find other fish in the sea
Can you believe he would still choose me?
Dear Dora, if only I had been given the chance and
Window of opportunity..
I would break every mold, rewrite every story
That's ever been told about "tradition" and with your
    permission...
To have and to hold him. Forever.

14

10,000 hours to Michelle Obama's Arm Muscles

VICKY OLIVER

I believe that the harder you work at something, the better you get at it. I live by Malcolm Gladwell's 10,000-Hour Rule. In short, 10,000 hours of deliberate practice are needed to become "world class" in any field. And then—like magical muscle memory kicking in to your forehand stroke during a game of tennis—suddenly, you are a force of nature.

Oh, sure, there are prodigies—the Mozarts of the world who compose their first piano concertos by the age of four and their first minuets by the tender age of six. But for the rest of us, there is no substitute for hard work.

To be clear, Malcolm Gladwell did not invent this rule—he described it in his book *Outliers* and made it simple to understand. The men who first wrote about it were Herbert Simon and William Chase in a published paper that appeared in *Scientific American* forty-seven years ago. Their dramatic revelation:

There are no instant experts in chess—certainly no instant masters or grandmasters.

I first learned about the 10,000 Rule in *Outliers*, yet it did not take Malcolm Gladwell for me to make this discovery. I believe that I stumbled on it on my own, which is why his theory resonates with me so deeply. As a child, I used to be pretty average in math. That is, until the fourth grade when I decided to apply myself. This is how I remember it.

I had memorized the multiplication table, all except for 7x4. Or maybe I knew that 7x4 was 28, but when I saw my mother staring me down during a Parents' Day math class at my all-girls school in Manhattan, I froze. Was 7x4... 28 or 32 or... I could not remember. My mother frowned at me, trying to will the right answer out of my mouth. But her dark eyes and dark skin would crumple up in disappointment.

"Is it 32?" I asked.

The teacher, Miss Profit, a tall, leggy, bespectacled woman with a penchant for long kilts, shook her blond coiffed head. "No, I'm sorry. The answer is 28."

A ripple went around the room from all the parents. This was a private school, after all. Could one of its students really be that dumb?

After that, my mother tested me every blessed day on multiplication. "What is 7x3?" she'd ask, accosting me as I walked in the door of our apartment.

"21. I'm late for ballet, Mom."

"Good! And 7x4?"

"28," I'd say, grabbing my pink toe shoes.

"Do you want to see a James Bond movie this weekend with me and John?"

"Yes."

"Great. What's 8x3?"

I worked so hard at mastering the multiplication table that a few months later Miss Profit called my parents back to the school to say she thought I was working too hard.

"I think you're pushing her too much," said Miss Profit. "Vicky gets nosebleeds each day right before class."

My mother told the teacher that I was "doing it to myself," that is, pressuring myself to excel. (Then my mother took me to the doctor to get my nose cauterized.)

Thomas Jefferson said, "I am a great believer in luck, and I find the harder I work, the more I have of it." To me, he meant that you don't actually need luck, per se. You acquire what others perceive as good fortune by diligently applying yourself to the task. Through rigorous application and hours of toil, you spot the connections that elude amateurs, uncover and refine the mental muscles you never knew you had, and you take a giant leap in your performance. Through diligence, you create your own luck.

If I spent 10,000 hours at a gym, I believe that I would be buff and have arm muscles to rival Michelle Obama's. You would, too. We all would.

The next time I remember really working hard at something was trying to get myself *out* of that school.

The odds did not look promising. My mother had graduated from the school and had glowing memories. Beyond that, her dream was to see me graduate from the school that she had only been fortunate enough to transfer into in the ninth grade. She had only had the chance to be a student there for four blissful years. But to me, she would give the gift of going for twelve!

However, there were numerous reasons I wanted out. To name a couple: mean girls and zero boys.

There were just as many reasons my mother wanted me to stay. To name a couple: it was her school, *dammit*, and I was her only daughter.

"It's only eight more years!" she would chirp like a cheerleader. "It will be over before you know it."

To me at the time, eight years sounded like Eternity. (After all, as I'd learned in math, if you wrote an 8 horizontally, it *was* infinity.) Thus, I went on a campaign to liberate myself from the school.

I looked up every single factoid I could find to make my case —the difference in college acceptances at this school versus the co-ed school in Manhattan I'd set my heart on. The difference between the science departments at the two schools. How the two dance departments compared. The theater departments. The girls' volleyball teams. My research was relentless. At one point, I discovered that the headmistress of my all-girls school was on the board of the other. "She must think it a pretty fine school," I reasoned. She could not keep me locked up like Rapunzel in the all-girls' Ivory Tower forever, not when she was on the board of the other school. That would be totally unfair.

This was before the internet existed, so finding out this information wasn't simple. And then, in the same manner that my mother had stopped me to drill me on multiplication, I stalked my parents each time they walked in the door.

First, I wrote down all the reasons that I should be allowed to transfer on a yellow legal pad. Then, each time my parents entered the apartment, I presented them with yet another reason.

For example:

"Reason number 5," I would say, holding up my hand like a sentry. "Their chemistry department is better."

"Make it stop," my mother said to my stepfather after the first fifteen reasons.

But I just wouldn't. I was the Energizer Bunny of reasons.

Ultimately, my mother claimed that I nagged her into

submission. And finally, five years later, she relented and allowed me to transfer.

My parents (all three of them) were account executives in the advertising business at the time. And whether through nurture or nature, I began to think of goal attainment in the form of long-term campaigns.

My next 10,000-hour campaign involved my efforts to get into an Ivy League college. I had my heart set on one in particular, and my PSAT scores were fantastic. But then, mysteriously, when it came around to the real decider, my SAT scores dropped by over 100 points in math (no surprise) and English. Ouch!

I asked my parents to hire a tutor for me.

Today, many kids with lackluster test scores hire tutors, but back then, this practice was uncommon. My parents, who were by then no strangers to my love-hate relationship with math, agreed that a tutor was a necessity. On my own volition, I spent every Saturday afternoon hunkered down inside the musty office of a middle-aged female tutor with a bowl-shaped haircut and pronounced body odor but a phenomenal eye for a kid's stumbling blocks. I took practice SAT after practice SAT. I turned down at least twenty invitations to toss a frisbee in Central Park. Boy, was I relieved when my test scores rose back to the PSAT levels.

As fate would have it, though, the original SAT scores weren't the only issue. At least twenty-five kids applied to the same college from my class of 100, thus some of my closest friends turned out to be my stiffest competition. These kids played tennis like they were vying for the French Open, spoke French like they had been raised in Paris, and jetted to Paris each summer instead of holding down babysitting jobs in New York like me. These kids were all more talented than me and worldlier. I had to do something to distinguish myself—but what?

Once again, I took the "nagging" approach to persuasion.

After meeting with the college interviewer for an hour and fifteen minutes, I decided to keep up the relationship. I sent him articles that I'd written for the school paper in giant roll tubes. I sent him postcards from a family vacation. And finally, I mailed him a photocopy of my interim report card. "Just a note to show you that my grade in Calculus AB actually went up this term, even though this report card doesn't count toward getting in."

The college admissions director at Brown University called the college guidance counselor at my high school and told him, "All we know is that Vicky really, really wants to come to Brown. We have no choice but to accept her."

After graduation, I longed to follow my parents into advertising, but they practiced a certain type of "tough love" that has long since fallen out of vogue. They did not help me get a job, and—possibly because our country was in a deep recession —I began my hallowed career as a receptionist at an advertising agency. (The other receptionist had received her MBA from Columbia University.)

My next goal achievement campaign began in earnest when, as a cub junior copywriter in direct response advertising, I dreamed of switching into the more glamorous side of the business: general advertising. On the direct side were poorly shot long-form commercials followed by scrolling 800 phone numbers to call. On the general side were high-production commercials of the 30-second variety, based on compelling ideas. The distinction between advertising's two halves continued into print, where on the direct side, ads were tested. Results alone dictated whether a print ad would run again, not the overall creativity of the ad. In the unholy alliance between art and commerce, direct leaned toward commerce.

This was one time in my life when I likely spent many, many more hours than 10,000—it may have been closer to 20,000 or even 30,000—and it was still impossible. I was told all sorts of things by well-meaning individuals, such as my boss, a wonderful, big-hearted man with a sharp eye for advertising copy and a Santa Claus laugh. His name was Bob. Bob told me that I made too much money and was "too good at direct" to ever make the switch. I was twenty-five years old. Were all paths closed to me, save for the one I was on? What about Led Zeppelin's assertion in "Stairway to Heaven" that you could still change your road?

Unfortunately, human resources professionals who interviewed me, from Young & Rubicam to BBDO, concurred with Bob and not Led Zeppelin. They said that now that I was in direct, I had attained "golden handcuffs" assuring that was where I would stay. The portfolio of advertisements I had created in direct was deemed to be too far away from the prettier, less coupon-laden print ads I wanted to write. A writer named Seth Godin, in his book called *The Dip,* analyzed when someone should quit a pursuit, and probably by his standards, I should have. Godin takes Vince Lombardi's inspirational wisdom and turns it on its head. "Quitters never win and winners never quit," Lombardi wrote. Godin tells us this is bad advice. "Winners quit all the time," according to Godin. "They just quit the right stuff at the right time."

I didn't.

I took class after class after class after class after class after class at the School of Visual Arts in an attempt to turn my direct response portfolio into a general advertising one. And one day, after a hundred reworkings of my portfolio, I was accepted into the hallowed halls of general advertising. I started my career all over again—at less than half the salary and with a deflated title—at Grey Advertising.

What about burnout, one might ask? Won't hurtling oneself at breakneck speed into a series of 10,000-hour campaigns hasten its onslaught? I was surprised to discover that a psychologist named Herbert Freudenberger invented the term "burnout" in 1974. In a cover story in *Association for Psychological Science* titled "Burnout and the Brain" that appeared in 2016, I learned that burnout is now considered a bona fide medical disorder. The article also states, "It's a common misconception that the culprit behind burnout is simply working too long or too hard." The culprit is a lethal combination of many factors. The article goes on to say, "burnout results when the balance of deadlines, demands, working hours, and other stressors outstrips rewards, recognition, and relaxation."

One day, about five years ago, I was at the RISD museum in Providence, Rhode Island, with a friend of mine from Brown. Somehow, we got to talking about Malcolm Gladwell's 10,000 Hour-Rule.

"Do you think I've already spent 10,000 hours?" I asked her. I was referring to my quest to become a writer. "I mean, I took all those copywriting classes at the School of Visual Arts. Then I took all the article writing classes at Gotham. Then I took all the novel writing classes at NYU. I've taken screenwriting classes and playwriting classes. I even took a poetry writing class once by mistake."

"You have spent much more than 10,000 hours," she said.

"Good," I said. "Then I guess the only thing to do is spend 10,000 more."

15

Cereal Killer
C. H. LINDSAY

Memories of childhood
fill each spoonful of cold cereal:
Spiderman,
Bugs Bunny,
Ninja Turtles.

Now grown, I cannot resist
the sugary treats in the cereal aisle:
Cocoa Puffs,
Honeycomb,
Captain Crunch.

Alone in the apartment,
I give in to temptation:
Darkwing Duck pajamas,
cartoon DVDs,
Tweety Bird bowl.

A perfect night for childlike laughter...
until the illusion shatters:
Three tiny weevils
float to the surface.
My childhood is ruined.

16

Missing Margaret
DONNA GRAVES

Sam Grayson put an unshelled peanut on the other side of the wrought iron table and settled back into his chair waiting for the bird to make a decision. Five feet away on the top of the privacy fence, the scrub jay jerked its head one way then another, eyeing the peanut. Sam put another nut beside the first one. "See. Two," he taunted. The jay took a few nervous hops along the fence and took off. How did Larry do it? Larry could get a jay to eat out of his hand. For a month now, Sam couldn't even get the bird to take a peanut off the table. *Oh well,* Sam sighed, *he'll be back. I'm not giving up.*

Grabbing one of the nuts, he cracked it and ate it himself, gazing out at the garden he'd made in his yard—the raised beds, the trellises, the waterfall that spilled into a little pond, and... the bird feeders. Margaret hated bird feeders. Wouldn't let him have one. He could still see the sour look on her face when she said, "They attract *rats.* You're not putting that up."

He took a deep breath and ran his long fingers across the top of his head. It was Saturday, and he needed a haircut, but with the weather cooler than usual, it would be a good day to work in the garden. Of course, if Margaret were here, she would insist he get the haircut. And she wouldn't like the idea of shaving it all off, either—something he was considering—getting rid of that old-man gray fringe, going for a more macho bald look. He missed Margaret. Not as much as some people thought. Intelligent, interesting, a good cook... He missed her conversations and her cooking, but he didn't miss that cantankerous streak when she set her mind on something. And he didn't miss the way she couldn't let things just happen. Days, weeks, months, seasons, year after year, Margaret planned their lives, putting marks on calendars in a frantic repetition of activities that left Sam yearning for a day like today with nothing to do but putter in the garden. Friends, sad to see a devoted couple parted by death, sent sympathy cards, asked if he needed anything, and invited him to dinner. Some even suggested he was still young—54 didn't seem young to Sam—and when he felt like meeting someone, they could arrange it. He politely declined their help and invitations. Recuperating from 23 years of a bustling social life, he luxuriated in the time alone.

In the four months since losing Margaret, he'd devoted himself to the garden. With no one to please but himself, he'd hung an Audubon hopper that looked like a little red house, a wire "squirrel-be-gone" feeder, a "humzinger" for the hummingbirds... and he put a bell on the cat. Soon jays, doves, warblers, chickadees, finches, and hummingbirds appeared. When the waterfall and pond were finished, magpies and robins came to bathe. In the evening or on a morning like today, he'd sit on the deck at peace with the world, delighting in his garden and the spectacle of nature's feathered creatures. Training a scrub jay to take a peanut from his hand was all that remained to make him perfectly happy. He'd seen people do it on YouTube. Even Larry —who wasn't particularly interested in birds—had done it. "The secret," Larry said, "is to leave a nut closer and closer until the jay no longer fears you."

So far, Larry's advice hadn't worked. It wasn't going to happen today. He might as well begin working in the garden. He lifted his hand to put the nut back in the bag, when a sudden rush of black feathers flew with startling speed down to the table. His hand jerked away. He froze, staring in astonishment at a large crow with a fearsome black beak and inquisitive brown eyes aimed at him. A split second of acknowledgment and the crow and the peanut were gone.

A crow? Sam had never seen a crow in the neighborhood. There were crows in the mountains where he fished, but… no, wait. He *had* seen a crow at the cemetery. With everything else going on, he hadn't thought much about it.

He'd been so busy at the funeral. He'd had to give Margaret's sisters pictures and things to display for the viewing room. For the center of the table, he'd chosen a photo of Margaret on their Mediterranean cruise ship laughing, her curly black hair flying in the wind, wearing those amusing little bee-shaped earrings she loved. Perhaps it wasn't formal enough for a funeral, but it was the way he wanted people to remember her. The reception line surprised him. Their friends came, of course, but people he barely knew or had never seen offered condolences, pressing his hand with intimate compassion while he struggled to place them. Was he/she one of Margaret's co-workers? An old school friend? It was all so tiring. The unexpected diagnosis. The scans. The blood tests. The chemo. The fight to keep Margaret alive. The struggle to be tender for her and strong for himself. Weary from a year of grief, he'd stood in the reception line greeting and smiling, wanting for it to be over. No wonder when the casket was lowered into the gravesite, he'd barely noticed the crow in the cemetery.

He searched the aspen branches and pine boughs one last time for signs of the crow when a tiny jingle sounded. Sam turned to see Margaret's cat bounding up the stairs of the deck toward him. A few scampering steps, a leap, and she landed in Sam's lap, rubbing her head on his thighs, purring and begging for attention. Sam pushed the furry creature away. No matter how much he discouraged her, the cat kept trying to cozy up to him. Always him. Not Margaret. And *he* was the one who was allergic. Just another annoyance. Margaret's irrational fear of mice wouldn't let her part with the cat, so Sam woke up sneezing every morning. Seven years of it. Now, why not get rid of the cat... but how? With no sign of the crow, he rose from his chair and went to work in the garden.

He didn't see the crow the next day either. Reading the Sunday *Trib* while sipping his coffee on the deck, he caught a glimpse of Margaret's cat pawing at something by the tomato plants. It appeared to be something soft. Had he left a garden glove there? Or could it be...? Fearing what the cat might have caught, he put down his coffee cup and dashed over to see. *A bird. A dead bird!* A flood of sentiment—sorrow for the lifeless robin, anger at the grey paws that played with it—poured into Sam. Kicking the cat aside, he picked up the delicate feathered remains then carried the dead robin and a shovel to the back corner of the yard where digging a hole to bury it, he grumbled, "You can't kill the birds. You can't be in the yard. Inside. That's where you'll stay. Inside."

On Monday, before going to work at the museum, Sam

cleaned the cat's litter box and filled its bowl with cat chow—the expensive organic kind that Margaret insisted on buying. The cat followed him, mewing with affection. How was he going to get rid of her? He couldn't dump her at the animal shelter. Would one of Margaret's friends take her? Who?

He was still wondering what to do with the cat when he arrived at the museum and saw Larry's short round figure hurrying towards him.

"They've come! *Two* days early," Larry blurted in breathless irritation. "And the abstracts are still *up*."

Why not Larry? He likes cats, and he loved Margaret. "Are you switching them today?" Sam asked.

"Today?" scoffed Larry, "Jesus Christ. I've got Kevin and Sara taking the abstracts down, and Alex and Ivy will help unpack the Latins. But how can we—"

"Well," Sam walked over to the elevator and pushed the down button, "let's do what we can."

It was four o'clock before the last Latin painting, a Rufino Tamayo, had been opened and examined. Sam knelt beside the painting admiring the power expressed in the open-mouthed dogs, their jagged teeth ready to rip apart an unseen victim. Who? What eminent disaster would complete the scene? Much more interesting than the abstracts, although Larry didn't think so—and neither would Margaret.

"That's it," Larry sighed. "We got it done. So, how was your weekend?"

Sam stood up, unfolding his body to its full 6 foot 2 inches, and looked down at Larry, whose height was not the greatest difference in the two men. "Would you like a cat, Larry?"

Behind the round plastic frames of his glasses, Larry studied Sam's blue eyes for a moment in bemused silence. "I can't take

Margaret's cat." He grinned. "I have two. And Oliver doesn't play well with others."

"Larry, she *killed* a bird. And," Sam pulled out a handkerchief from his pocket and wiped his runny nose, "she makes me sneeze. I'll have to give her to the shelter. You know how much she meant to Margaret."

"You and birds," Larry shook his head and—ignoring the play on his friendship with Margaret—asked, "Did you get the jay to take a peanut?"

"No. But a crow came out of nowhere. Took a peanut right off the table in front of me."

"Really? I don't think I've ever seen a crow in the valley. However, crows will fly 20 miles every day from their murder." Larry—who shared Margaret's love for trivia—began pulling up facts. "A murder," he said raising one finger in the air to emphasize the information, "is a group of crows. A crow will leave its murder during the day—fly to a place to fed, forage, or whatever—then return to roost with the murder at night. They're smart. They can solve problems and use tools. It would be interesting to see what you could get a crow to do. Try feeding it."

Sam went home wondering if he would die before Margaret's cat did. Although fifty-four wasn't that old, it was possible. Margaret was forty-six when she died. He poured himself a cocktail and, making sure the cat stayed inside, walked out on the deck. As soon as he sat down, he heard a loud insistent *CAW-CAW-CAW*. Looking up, he saw the crow sitting on a branch peering down at him from the Austrian pine that bordered the back of his property.

Why not? Remembering what Larry suggested, he decided to try to feed the crow.

The crow cawed again.

Sam dashed to the kitchen and grabbed the bag of peanuts sitting on the counter. When he pulled the sliding door open to go back outside, the cat tried to get out too, but Sam managed to shut the door to keep her inside. He took the plastic bag of unshelled nuts over to the table and poured several out in a pile. Immediately, the crow dropped down beside them and picked one up. Sam watched astonished as maneuvering the nut further into its mouth, the crow picked up another one... and another one. With three peanuts clasped tightly in its beak, the crow flew away.

Amazing! Sam's skin tingled in excitement. The crow had come within arm's reach. Oh, if only Margaret were here to see the crow take three peanuts at once! He wanted to tell someone. There was no one here, though, except... He turned his head around and saw the cat behind the glass door twitching its tail, glaring at the pine tree.

The crow didn't come back that evening.

"Three at once!" Sam told Larry the next day.

"Try making it take one from your hand. It's really not that hard," Larry said with a tinge of superiority cloaked in a mentoring manner.

On his way home from work that day, Sam stopped at Noodles and got a dish of chicken *cavatappi*. He ate it alone in the restaurant. It wasn't as good as Margaret's. Nothing he cooked or bought was. As much as he missed her food and her company, he still looked forward to going home to his garden and his birds. This evening he would see if the crow would take a peanut from his hand.

As he had the night before, he filled a small glass with ice and poured in enough Jack Daniels to cover the cubes then took the cocktail and the bag of peanuts out on the deck. A few finches hopped from perch to perch on the wire feeder pecking out seeds. Two hummingbirds, fighting for territorial rights, buzzed and chased each other away from the *hummzinger.* In quick jerks of stop-look-and-go, a squirrel dashed around the Austrian pine's trunk then scampered down to the top of the waterfall for a drink. Pink, red, purple, and orange zinnias, yellow sunflowers, tomatoes ripening on vines, the scent of sweet basil and rosemary... It was a perfect evening. Would Margaret love it? Oh, she would. She would she see how happy —a tomato?

A tomato rolled out of the raised garden bed. Sam's brows furrowed in confusion. A tomato leaping out of its bed by itself? Just as he saw the cause—a tan-colored rat—he heard a loud *CAW* followed by a short pause and another loud *CAW.* The crow landed with a little bounce on the table and stared expectantly at Sam. The rat was forgotten.

Beautiful and frightening, its black audacious eyes—daring him? beseeching him?—bored into Sam's. Slowly and carefully, Sam removed one peanut from the bag and held it out to the crow. Like royalty accepting its due, the crow lifted the peanut out of Sam's fingers with its beak—a long dangerous ebony beak. Sam could hardly breathe. The crow was so close he could touch it, so close he could see flecks of violet blue on its crown and small silky black feathers layered like scales on its back. If Sam moved, would it flap those tarry dark wings and disappear? No, the crow knew what it wanted. Sam took another peanut from the bag and held it out to the crow. With one adroit move, the crow's beak lifted the nut out of Sam's fingers. Then, as Sam watched in amazement, the crow dropped the peanut and grabbed it with a claw, keeping it steady on the table while hacking at the shell with its beak. Three times Sam offered a nut to the crow, and three times the crow cracked the nut and ate it in front of Sam before flying away.

Sam smiled to himself. He'd done it. He leaned back in his chair and let the steel springs gently rock him while he finished his cocktail and reveled in the pleasures of his backyard garden. He wished Margaret were sitting beside him, but if she were... *Well,* he sighed, *there'd be no garden.* She'd have him hiking, biking, playing tennis, meeting with people to go to the opera or dinner, to the movies, or even to a foreign country. They had taken vacations—a Mediterranean cruise, a Hong Kong-to-China excursion, a trip to Machu Picchu—with friends. The more people, the more commotion and confusion, the more Margaret loved it. Would it have been different if they'd had children? He saw himself playing with the kids and taking care of the yard, but he couldn't picture Margaret as a homebody. Like so many other things, their lives hadn't turned out quite the way he'd imagined. He always thought he'd grow old with Margaret. He caught his breath then let it out slowly. No use thinking about it. He had the garden and the birds. He'd even hand fed one. It wasn't a jay. But that's the way things were.

Sam finished his drink and checked to see how much damage the rat had done to his tomatoes. What was he to do? Poison and traps might kill the birds. Gathering a few tomatoes and balancing them together with his empty glass, he went back to the house and slid open the patio door—the cat! Damn!

She'd gotten out and disappeared.

Two weeks passed, and there was no sign of her, but the crow came back every day. Sam might be pulling weeds from between the bean and tomato plants, pinching back the basil and rosemary, or enjoying the pungent sweet smell of the herbs when with a sudden bounce, an inky black apparition would appear on the railing of the deck, cawing, fidgeting, and puffing out its feathers until Sam came to feed it. At first, the routine was the same. The crow would either take a nut from Sam's hand, crack it, and eat it there, or fly away with it and return for another.

Then, one Saturday morning, seeing what looked like two red-capped house finches at the feeder, Sam took his breakfast, a bowl of Honey Nut Cheerios, out onto the deck. He hadn't been there long watching the finches and enjoying the delicate pings of their birdsong when the crow landed on the table with a loud demanding squawk. Reluctant to leave his breakfast to get peanuts, Sam spooned more cereal into his mouth. "I have to eat *my* food first," he told the crow. The bird's shiny eyes bored into Sam's. No longer able to stand it, Sam dumped some Cheerios off his spoon. "Try some," he said. The crow cocked its head one way then the other before deciding to take the cereal. Sam ate a few more spoonfuls and gave the rest to the crow.

Now Sam had an eating companion. From his research on the internet, he learned that the crow would eat fruit, nuts, eggs, pasta, pasta filled with peanut butter, whole grain bread, plain popcorn, cat food, chili, and banana peppers. He tried all these things. Setting up a plate for the crow and one for himself, they dined together. As soon as Sam sat down to eat, the crow would join him. Sam would dish out the food and begin a conversation. He might say:

"Try the eggs. It's all right, no chickens were harmed in gathering them."

OR

"I stopped at Noodles and we're having *cavatappi* tonight. I think you'll like it."

OR

"What do you think of the cat food? It's organic. You haven't seen the cat, have you?"

OR

"I bought these just for you. They're too hot for me. What do you think? Wow. You really do like chili peppers!"

OR

"How did your day go? Mine was fine. Almost. The director wants to buy another minimalist piece. It's six pieces of lumber arranged as a cross on the floor. Can you imagine? I could have picked up some lumber at Home Depot and thrown that together myself. "

Or any other table small talk he thought he and the crow might enjoy.

He didn't tell Larry—he wanted to surprise him. But after two weeks of keeping his secret to himself, he decided to invite Larry over for dinner and introduce him to Ed. While he never called the cat the name Margaret gave her, Missy, he liked calling the crow Ed.

Larry *was* surprised, surprised that Sam asked him to dinner, surprised that Sam could *cook*. "I'll bring spinach puffs. You always liked my spinach puffs," Larry said, accepting the invitation. "You know," he added, "this is a good. It's time you started socializing again. Who else is coming?"

"Just you, me, and Ed. You don't need to bring anything."

"Who's Ed?" Larry blinked.

"You'll see."

Larry looked warily at Sam. "This—this isn't an attempt to set me up with Ed, is it? You know I hate this matchmaking stuff. The last time Margaret tried to—"

Sam shook his head. "I'm not setting you up. Just come. Next Saturday. You'll see."

Saturday afternoon, a small dead rat, like an overture to disaster, lay on the deck. What now? Where did it come from? When Sam went out to get rid of it, he heard a familiar *jingle*. A moment later, Margaret's cat was by his side rubbing her head against his leg and mewing. With unexpected happiness, he found himself bending over and lifting her up to his chest. "Where have you been? " he said, rubbing his fingers through her fur. "I suppose the rat is yours, huh? Come on." He sneezed. "Let's get you something good to eat." He filled a bowl with organic cat food and put it and the cat in the laundry room, closing the door, and left to clean up for Larry's visit.

First, he removed the rat, pulled some weeds, and swept the deck. Then, he took a shower. Having made the yard and himself presentable, he arranged a platter of fruit, prepared three individual side salads, and put the *cavatappi* in the oven to warm. With ten minutes to spare, he found Margaret's favorite blue plaid tablecloth—perfect for casual dining outside, she'd said— and covered the deck's patio table. Nothing remained except the wine. He opened the pinot noir and poured himself a glass. Promptly at six, Larry—who was never late—arrived.

"Where is this new friend of yours?" Larry asked, taking the glass of red wine Sam handed him.

"Oh, he'll show up when we're ready to eat."

Larry raised an eyebrow, but not wishing to be critical of someone he hadn't met, he didn't comment on Ed's behavior. Instead, he turned the conversation to the office, wanting to know how Sam liked the new director's ideas to improve the museum. When Sam didn't seem interested in discussing work, Larry brought up the subject of Sam's new life. "Why don't you ask Ivy out? She's a nice gal. Besides," Larry gave Sam a devilish grin, "I think she has the hots for you. I see the way she looks at you."

"I'm not ready for that. Let me show you what I've been doing," Sam said, leading the way out to the garden.

Larry, seeing what Sam had done, shook his head and laughed. "What a difference. Margaret wasn't much in to gardening, was she? And the bird feeders... You never had those before. By the way, have you been able to feed peanuts to that jay?"

"No... but this crow. You said crows are smart and it would be interesting to see what I could get a crow to do. You were right. I've always loved birds. Loved looking at them. Listening to them sing. But this crow... It takes my appreciation of birds to a whole new level. He's so smart. It makes me wonder if the military has ever tried to train crows. I've heard they've tried to train dolphins. Why not crows?" Sam cracked a big smile. "Crows spying on North Korea, wouldn't that be a great Tom Clancy novel! "

"I'd read it," Larry grinned.

"You've seen the garden. Let's get started on dinner," Sam said gesturing towards the kitchen.

"And your friend?" Larry took a quick look at his watch.

"Oh, he'll be here," Sam said and led the way into the house.

While Sam poured more wine and sliced the French bread, Larry headed for the bathroom to wash his hands. On the way, he passed the laundry room and heard the cat meowing. "My goodness, is that Margaret's kitty?" he asked, impulsively opening the door. "Missy." He reached down to pet her.

"Oh no!" Sam shouted, "Don't let her—"

Before he could say "out," a streak of flying fur had disappeared down the hall, around the corner, and into a room full of couches, tables, desks, chairs, bookcases, media consoles, baskets, stacks of magazines, and random boxes being sorted.

Larry began pushing aside boxes. "Missy, Missy," he called.

Sam looked in the room and sighed. "Forget it. She could have run through this room and gone upstairs or downstairs. Let's eat."

"We're eating without Ed?"

"I think he'll show up."

"Interesting," Larry said. Shaking his head in disbelief, he took the plate of *cavatappi* that Sam handed him and carried it out to the deck. Once all the food was on the table, including the plate Sam had dished up for Ed, Larry said, "Were Margaret and Ed friends?"

"No. Margaret wouldn't have liked him."

"Why not?"

"Well—"

CAAAAAW came the scream.

Jumping back from the mass of black feathers that landed on the table, Larry's fork flew out of his hand.

The crow bounced, cocked its head, and sunk its beak into a *cavatappi* noodle.

Larry yanked his napkin off his lap and snapped it at the crow. "My god, he's eating Ed's dinner! Get him out of here!"

"No, no," Sam said, pushing Larry's hand down. "He *is* Ed."

Larry frowned at Ed, who had retreated to the top of the privacy fence. The crow's shiny brown eyes peered ominously back.

"I've been eating dinner with him every night. He's so smart, Larry. He's like a person. I think he could be trained to do amazing things."

"Really?" Larry kept his eyes on the crow, whose feathers were puffing up. "Like what?"

"I don't know yet. I need time to think about it. What do you think?"

"Me?" Larry huffed, "I think your time would be better spent with Ivy. You need a real person, not a crow, to replace Margaret."

What? Larry thinks Ed is meant to replace Margaret? Ed is a project, not a replacement. He is... Sam looked at Ed. The crow was taking little agitated hops right and left along the fence. His wings fluttered then sprung out to their full width. Several swift wing motions took the crow from the fence to the branch of an Aspen where he perched, peering down at Sam and Larry. There was no time for the two men to think about how to proceed with dinner before the crow made a dive straight for Larry.

"What the hell!?" Larry's hands flung up to protect his face.

Ed swooped down, poked his beak into Larry's head then zoomed up and circled the air for another dive. Larry ran inside, hoping to go through the house and escape out the front door, but Ed flew after him and smacked his claws on the back of Larry's head. Larry snatched a pillow from the couch and swung it in circles while the crow kept buzzing him. "Sam!" he screamed. "Get it away from me!"

The way to the front door was free. Sam opened it, and Larry ran out with Ed flying after him. Sam closed the door and watched out the window at Larry's chubby body flopping as he ran down the hill to his car. Just as Ed made a final lunge, Larry got in the car, slammed the door, and drove away, leaving Ed in the parking strip's sycamore tree flapping his wings. Thinking Ed might come back inside, Sam hustled to the kitchen and closed the sliding door.

What had happened? He couldn't imagine a worse outcome. He'd wanted Larry to be charmed by Ed, not attacked. Feeling like he needed it, he filled a small glass with ice and Jack Daniels then sat in a kitchen chair looking out at the scene of the disaster where the plate of fruit, the salads, the *cavatappi*, and the half-empty wine glasses sat abandoned on Margaret's cheerful blue tablecloth until Ed arrived to enjoy the feast.

Meow.

Margaret's cat trotted over to him and rubbed her head playfully against his shins. Sam gathered her up and held her on his lap, petting and soothing her, while Ed picked at noodles and tore at strawberries. When Ed finished, he hopped over to the sliding door and struck his beak against the glass. "Oh, Missy," Sam sighed, "I miss Margaret. What am I going to do now?" Missy looked up at him and purred.

17

Obituary
SUE STEVENSON LETH

Back in 38 when times were hard, had a Colt 45 and a deck of
cards:
Denton Benson

Mother never forgave my father for killing himself
in their shiny new Great Gatsby Ford with a rag top
and running boards.

Owned the town with a bar and grill,
could suck the life from a dollar bill:
Denton Benson

That "other woman" in the car, Dorothy Jones so the
    papers
said, made a horrible time even more awkward with me
waiting to be born.

He wore wing tip shoes with snow white
spats, a diamond pinky ring and a silk cravat:
Denton Benson

Mother locked him in a box and put him in the basement,
would never let him out. He's been thumping around
    in our
lives ever since.

A black granite tombstone bears his name,
the Chat and Chew his claim to fame:
Denton Benson

Took his black leather wallet and a photograph, hung
    him on
the wall labeled loneliness, "Never let me see that
    again," she
told me.

A carved brave mustache and dark level eyes,
a full-lipped stranger always makes me cry.
Denton Benson

18

Unforgettable

ELIZABETH SUGGS

Chandra was a lonely old woman with a bent-over back and hunched shoulders. On one not so special day, she walked over to a pond beside her house and stepped inside. Floating over to the center of the pool, she drew in a deep breath and plunged her head under the water's surface.

Sometimes she held her breath, just to see how long she could keep herself underwater before the spasms of pain forced her back up, gasping and heaving for breath. It helped her remember she was alive. Only, this time was different. This time, there was no pain. She was underwater for thirty seconds, then one minute, then five minutes. She was weightless. She held her breath for ten minutes. An hour. She didn't require breath, not anymore, bobbing up just below the surface, her back facing the world. No one would be looking for her, not for days. Months. She could hide in the water forever, and no one would come.

But then someone did come. A man in black. He pulled her body up from the water and set her on the grass.

"I didn't kill myself," she said. For some reason, this seemed important to say. As if all her past sins could be washed away by this one truth. She hadn't done it, had she? Not intentionally.

"I know," he replied. His voice was thick, deep. It seemed to echo, as if two voices spoke, one inside her mind and one outside. "But, it's time." His colorless eyes watched her.

"Do they hate me?" She thought of her children, her friends, strangers, anyone who looked upon her and had chosen to turn away without so much as a smile.

He shook his head. Was that a lie? It would be too easy if it was. Chandra decided he didn't look like a liar. "They have just forgotten to care."

In a way, that was worse. At least someone hated was remembered.

"Will you forget me?" she whispered, barely understanding what she said. Since the man arrived, she had forgotten which were thoughts and which were words.

"No," he said. This time softer. Comforting, like a mother with a babe. "I've never forgotten you. I saw you when you were born, and I see you now. I've been waiting for this day. It's taken too long. I'm sorry for the delay."

She nodded. He seemed familiar somehow, or maybe that's what she wanted to believe. If he wasn't a stranger, she could walk off with him without chastising herself later.

"Chandra," he whispered.

She looked up at him. His hand extended toward her. What would happen if she didn't take it? Would she go back to her life? Back to… what? She looked up at her house. It was a small home, big enough for one. Big enough for isolation.

She turned back to the man. He was younger than she, with only slight wrinkles around his mouth and eyes: *smile lines*. She hadn't smiled in years.

"I'll make you smile again," he said. His tone was so

soothing, so familiar. She was sure she had seen him somewhere. A distant memory, perhaps. If she just had a little longer with him, maybe she could remember where she knew him.

She took his hand. She would just go on a walk with him, just for a little while.

19

Eulogy for My Living Brother
SARA WETMORE

My brother is dead, yet his body roams free. In his skin, a monster crawls. I'm reminded of parasites, the kind that hijack the host's nervous system, reanimating the dead remains of insects and rewiring them for destruction. They lead the zombie insect back to its nest and infect the entire colony. Soon, the colony collapses, with only a single parasite to blame.

I believe opioids react the same way. They take a living, breathing human that is suffering, latch onto them, and lie in wait. Then, when the mind is gone, they enslave the host, forcing it to commit atrocities until the family perishes with it.

In 2017 alone, nearly 30,000 Americans died of drug overdose related to fentanyl and synthetic opioids[1]. And those are just the ones whose bodies succumb. Countless others, including my dear brother, are lost each year. The essential part of their being departs from this earth, and often they do not return.

It wasn't always this way. Though my brother, much like our entire family, has always been disturbed by some unspoken shadow, he was once—at least outwardly—a very happy kid. He was always laughing or making a joke, desperate to bring joy to those around him. In fact, you may struggle to conjure up a memory of him when he was younger in which he wasn't being silly. When I close my eyes and think of him then, all I feel is warmth.

In old photographs, we are seen together smiling, his arm wrapped around me tightly as he pulled me into the purest embrace. He looks at the camera, his brown eyes sparkling beneath his cropped chocolate hair. I knew he loved me then, even though I was the younger sister, but I was the only sibling he had, and for that he was grateful to have an audience—any audience—for his playful affectations.

I looked up to him profoundly, wishing that somehow, I could make people laugh as easily as he did. I know he did it to impress people, but it was always so natural and so unbelievably funny that I swore he could be a comedian so great he would grace the ranks of such outstanding comics as Jim Carrey or Robin Williams.

I remember when we were children swimming at my aunt's swimming pool, he'd make all of our cousins laugh by pretending to be a whale. He'd launch himself out of the water like a torpedo, go stiff as a board, and then crash back into the water, splashing our faces as he made his best whale noises. My cousins laughed hysterically and copied what he was doing to less comedic effect.

There was another time when my cousins slept over at our house and, just as we were getting ready to go to sleep, my brother jumped out of the closet shouting, "I love the Furby! I love the Furby like the dickens! Hello, Billy!"

The words were random and made no sense to anyone but him, but he hid in the closet for well over an hour to make the joke. It was received with screams and giggles, and even decades later, my cousins will quote my brother saying this absurd line.

He was always surrounded by friends when he was growing up, and I admired him for that, too. Others were also entranced by his goofball antics, simply because he was so much fun to be around. An hour in his presence, and your cheeks would ache from peeling your mouth into its widest smile, your throat gasping for air as you tried to recover from his last joke. Being his friend was an exercise in stamina, constantly testing the threshold for humor in the human body.

As he got more friends, he paid less attention to me, and for that I got jealous and did everything I could to impress his little gang. At the age of five, I recall my brother and his friend picking up pebbles from the ground in our back yard and stuffing them into their nostrils. They would fill their bellies full of air, place their finger over their empty nostril, and then, in one powerful gust, blow the pebbles out as far as they could, boogery little rocks scattering across the cement. He told me to leave him alone, as he was clearly hanging out with his friend and couldn't be bothered with his little sister at the moment. But I didn't take no for an answer.

Eager to amaze, I took the largest pebble I could find and lodged it far back into my nose.

"Oh yeah? Watch this!" I exclaimed, puffing my chest and gearing up for launch.

They waited to see what I could do, but when I tried to blast the rock from my nostril, nothing moved. I tried again, pushing as much air against the pebble as I could muster over and over again. It wouldn't budge. My brother's friend laughed at me, and though I don't remember if my brother laughed too, I couldn't help but feel like I let him down. My inability to snot-rocket pebbles was shameful, so much so that the rock remained fixed deep in my nasal cavity for more than a week until our mother had to help me remove it. I started to bother him and his friends less after that.

As we got older, he got more friends. They became the center of his universe, always taking precedence over school or family. His grades slipped, and my parents would get frustrated with him, but I was still proud to be his sister. I didn't have many friends, so his growing group of companions was just another reason I admired him. In fact, I assumed he was very popular. With a personality like his, how could he not be? However, I had no glimpse into his reality. My perception was so skewed by my idea of him that I missed altogether the signs that he was struggling.

When we were in high school, my brother briefly owned an old, pale blue van. The doors would stick, and its polish was gone, but miraculously, the engine still functioned. As long as you remembered to put in a little bit of gas, it would get you where you needed to go. It wasn't a luxurious car by any means, but I still envied him because he could drive and I could not.

One day, he must have been distracted when he arrived at school and parked the van. I don't recall if he left the keys inside with the car running or if he just dropped them nearby, but someone took notice and decided to pull a cruel prank on him. When he came back outside to get in his van and drive home, it was gone. At first, he thought someone must have stolen it, but at some point, he realized that they had just moved it to get a reaction out of him, which wasn't hard to do.

He came home in a furious rage. After he walked through the front door, he slammed it behind him and stormed downstairs to his room, all the while screaming, "Fuck!"

My mother chased after him to see what was wrong, but all I

could hear was him sobbing and screaming at her, "Leave me the hell alone!"

My brother had always had a temper, and he was easily roused to rage. I never tempted it myself, as it was terrifying to witness, but I'm guessing other people did because this wasn't the last time he was the victim of a practical joke.

Later that year, he was nominated for Homecoming King. At the time, I wasn't surprised. I thought he was so cool and funny that of course he was nominated. I even voted for him on the ballot, sure that he could secure enough votes to win. But when I arrived home and went to congratulate him, he was clearly upset. He wouldn't tell me why, so I asked my mother.

"He was placed on the ballot as a joke," she said. The punchline was completely lost on me.

I had misread his life entirely, not understanding that perhaps the reason he placed so much value in his friends was because he felt lucky to have someone be friendly to him at all. This made it all the more devastating when, Jake, his closest friend whom he had known and trusted since childhood, died tragically in a car accident at the age of 20.

The years that followed Jake's passing were especially difficult on him, and it pained me to watch him coiled with his depression. Though he was never a religious person, I caught him reading the Bible, possibly searching for answers as to why God could thieve his best friend from this earth and leave him to cope alone. This should have been the first of many indications that he was distressed. Maybe if we had started paying more attention at this moment in time and tried to get him help, he would have resisted the temptation to withdraw from reality—resisted the siren song of opioids, and later, heroin.

Over time, the wounded memory of his friend's death scabbed over, and he began to find solace in his small but tight group of allies. Yet, they started to scatter, finding other opportunities outside of the city or moving forward in their lives, devoting themselves to their girlfriends and families or focusing solely on their careers. My brother had no girlfriend or career to speak of, and so he found other friends, ones with whom he could watch sports and smoke weed as he stumbled through existence.

He became more irritable in the years that followed Jake's death. Something as simple as not being able to open a bag of chips would result in him throwing the bag on the kitchen floor, cursing loudly, punching a wall, and stomping down the stairs so he could cool down in his room.

While his temper festered, he abandoned his identity as the funny guy and ultimately stopped smiling altogether. He became severe and found little to no joy in any of the things that he once loved. Rather than admiring him as I once did, I grew afraid of him. He often snapped at the slightest inconvenience, and it seemed better to steer clear of him lest I witness his shouting fury. His face would bloom into vibrant crimson, his veins fluttering like the petals of a vengeful flower, and his teeth bared like thorns primed to cut and bleed anyone that disturbed his space. He pushed his family away, even though we only wanted to help him. He did not see how much we cared.

Things got exponentially worse after the winter he fell during his early twenties. It was an especially wet season with the snow falling as rapidly as it melted. Puddles of vanquished snow would freeze over, only to be snowed upon once more, hiding their slippery menace. When fresh snow had fallen, my brother would shovel the driveway and clear a path to the front door early in the morning. He was helpful that way, even when the depression settled in.

One particular morning, he was out shoveling the walks

when his foot slipped on the ice, sending him soaring backwards and pounding his spine hard upon the frosty pavement. My brother being a towering giant, standing at about six-foot four and with as much grace as a young puppy, fell from an even greater height given his stature. He came back limping into the house, grunting in pain, his arm pressed against his back as he made his way to the living room couch to lie down. He was in severe pain, and unfortunately, that pain didn't dissipate over time.

Years after this fall, I noticed his discomfort and asked if he was okay.

"Yeah, it's just this damn back pain," he said.

He tried everything from ibuprofen and inversion tables to foam rollers and electrotherapy. Nothing seemed to work, which explains why he would turn to something stronger. At first, I imagine he just got hooked on pharmaceuticals to alleviate his back pain, but he also kept company with a new and unfamiliar crowd—all of whom were clearly into drugs, varying in severity. He was also the type of person that was eager to please, so if someone offered him anything, however dubious, to ease the discomfort he felt both physically and psychologically, I believe he'd scarcely decline.

By the time my brother was nearly thirty, we missed the signs that he was using heroin for nearly a year. Distracted by the loss of my father's job, my mother began working more hours to pay the bills. I was working full-time and had just moved in with my boyfriend, making me generally unaware of what occurred in my parents' home, and therefore, my brother's life. I try to tell myself that maybe if I had made more of an effort to be involved, I might have noticed when my already slender brother became gaunt and ghostly. I might have given heed to his comings and goings, taking note of unfamiliar patterns or his increased secrecy. But I wasn't. We were all so engrossed in our own particular dramas that we failed to observe his descent into darkness.

By the time we realized what was happening, it was too late. My parents repeatedly confronted him about his drug use, insisting that what they were seeing, what they were smelling, was not simply marijuana. There was something considerably more evil consuming him.

My mom pounded on his bedroom door, which he had locked to keep my parents away from him.

"Do you think I'm stupid?" my mom said to him. "I know you're using something, so why don't you just come out and tell me what it is?"

Though his depression was no secret before we discovered the truth, the signs were too prevalent to ignore. No longer sad, he was pure anger—a furious wall of fire that swelled with each passing day. Wanting nothing but the independence to intoxicate himself in peace, he blamed my parents for everything. How dare they inquire into their son's blatant drug use? How could they doubt his paper thin lies? More importantly, how impossibly rude that they would try to intervene when they discovered that their one and only son was, in fact, addicted to heroin.

They tried to save him in every way they knew how, but without health insurance or the funds to send him to rehab, their options were limited. They tried getting angry, but that just pushed him farther away. They tried kindness and understanding, but that just enabled him. They insisted that he sign up for any program that might help, but he dragged his feet and ultimately abandoned any plans to follow through.

To his credit, in the beginning, he did attend meetings for addiction as he tried to get sober, but this progress was derailed when he met his first long-time girlfriend, Krissy. She was also a recovering addict, and through their chance meeting, they began to get to know one another, exploring struggles that I could not fathom. But their magnetic attraction pushed more than it pulled. They began to flounder together, always oscillating between high and sober, never arriving at a permanent solution.

Not long after they started dating, she moved in with him, both of them dwelling in my parent's basement. Suddenly, my parents were outnumbered, facing not just one addict but two. And together, they tested my parents' patience. Unfortunately, when you love an addict, they almost always have the upper hand. They use your love for them as a weapon, stocking it with their perceived weakness and dependency. And with this gun to their heads, my parents were faced with an impossible choice: letting their son and his girlfriend use heroin in their household, hoping that one day they would truly get help and realize sobriety, or kicking them out and changing the locks, forcing their son into homelessness and constantly questioning whether he was still alive.

My parents tried both, each without success. Without consistency in their treatment of my brother's addiction, they were held hostage by their love for him, and in captivity they remain, with no clear answers on how to guide their son to temperance, as if it were like leading a horse to water.

The best way to deal with addiction is neither definite nor precise, and with something as insidious as heroin, even specially developed programs can often fail if the person suffering doesn't truly want to be sober. My parents, like many others, have not failed as guardians. They've done everything they can, given the circumstances, and my brother's sobriety should not fall on their shoulders. And yet, it does. I see them carry this burden with him, poisoning each of them against the other indefinitely. The parasite infects the host. The host infects the colony. The colony collapses. And so it goes until my brother chooses life over death.

I don't claim to have the answers. I did not tell this story to inspire, for this is not a story of triumph. It is a story of recovery which has failed repeatedly but cycles again and again.

My brother is still an addict, and will forever be, long after he gets clean. His struggle will not cease, but that does not make recovery impossible. Despite what others say, I believe he can come back from the dead. I have to believe he can. More importantly, I have to find it in my soul to forgive him for the damage he has wrought, for the pain he has caused my parents, and the blame with which he's afflicted them.

The alternative is to continue to grieve what we've lost: the dutiful son that shoveled the driveway early in the morning; the funny kid with all the friends, blowing rocks out of his nose to make you smile; the little boy with his arm wrapped around his younger sister, inspiring her with his charisma without ever knowing it.

---

1. Source: National Institute on Drug Abuse

20

Beyond the Blossoms
GRACE DIANE JESSEN

On a bright October day,
when I occupied a room
in the hospital's maternity wing
for the fifth time,
a nurse brought in a bouquet
and placed it near my bed.
Fresh yellow and white daisies,
small pink roses greeted me.
Tiny pink satin diapers on sticks
poked up here and there
with sprigs of green
above a shiny ribbon bow.
The card tucked in had been
signed by my husband's hand.
Astonished, knowing the balance
in our checkbook, but delighted
by the unexpected, I found
a tissue and dabbed my eyes.

Like trumpets echoing
in the coliseum of my heart,
the flowers announced that he
loved our baby daughter,
the other four at home,
and loved me, too, even though
we still did not have a son.

21

Winds of Fate

KRYSTAL C. GERBER

Heartbeats away from commencing the Choosing of the Heir, chills of dread were shooting down my spine. One of the breezes that were always ruffling my bronze curls and delivering glimpses of truth whispered in my ear: *heirs, bedlam, war. Knives. Secrets. This is a day of destiny and secrets.*

Two gold coffin-like doors opened from the inside, and I stepped into the grand throne room, the gilt walls echoing with the sound of my slippered footfalls. The cavernous, glittering room was covered in golden mirrors built to reflect light in every direction as well as magnify sound. The echoes were supposed to represent the far-reaching consequences of important decisions made in the throne room, but really they just rendered the huge space impractical for all but the smallest groups and softest voices.

At one end of the room was an empty throne draped in mourning lavender, honoring the emperor after his assassination the week prior. Before the throne, three young people stood in order of age. The heirs, two princes and a princess, had been waiting for an hour for me to arrive as was customary. Now they would have to wait a little longer, as all ten royal councilors—as well as a handful of guards—shuffled into the room as quietly as possible.

Watching the procession, I was relieved to see Councilor Jonse had returned in time for the ceremony. I needed a friend like a condemned man needs a pardon, and Jonse had given both advice and sympathy on many occasions. The rest of the councilors, like Councilor Ioka, were acquaintances who knew me only as Grand Sieve Arissa Mariosa, magical prodigy. High above the councilors' heads, the windows were thrown open, ensuring that there was a constant wind blowing through the room and carrying its secrets past me.

Feeling as desperate as a mouse trapped in the hawk mews, I took advantage of the shuffling people's slowness, mentally combing through the faint breeze while trying to think of a way out of this unholy mess. As Grand Sieve at only nineteen, I was far too inexperienced to pick an heir for the Empire, yet that is exactly what duty demanded I do. I would have given my liver on a spoon to the person who would choose the Emperor or Empress in my place, but only I could use the winds to pick the right heir. Short of my own suicide, I had to decide, and I already knew there was no right choice.

Wind is the only element to travel through time as well as space, and those sensitive to its whisperings were given snippets of possible futures to come as well as glimpses of the past. One gifted with the wind had to perfect their mental sieve as well as put up barriers to prevent going mad from a deluge of information.

A Grand Sieve's gift, however, is rare and powerful. Simply put, I use a finer net, a more sensitive mental sieve. A greater number of insights come to me, and I can to some extent find what I'm looking for. Which is why it is a Grand Sieve's job to pick the heir upon the death of the emperor.

In the past, the heir most thirsty for the throne would bribe a Sieve to name them Emperor or Empress. However, this always seemed to end in calamity for both the Sieve and the heir. The Empire and its emperors were closely tied to the elements, which had prevented tyrannical emperors from living long. Those that misused their power tended to lose it in terrible ways.

The last time the wrong heir had been chosen by a bribed Sieve, the elements of the Empire had risen against the wrongful emperor, burying him alive in a violent landslide during a military campaign, the logs submerged in the tumbling earth suddenly bursting into flames that wouldn't quench. Needless to say, going against the truthful heir had not been attempted for centuries. Nor did anyone argue with the Grand Sieve's word when spoken in the Choosing of the Heir ceremony, no matter how outlandish the Sieve's reasons for whom they chose to rule.

The late Emperor Timos had been the obvious choice thirty years ago, even had my predecessor not sifted the winds and known for certain. Timos was just and gentle, with sparkling blue eyes and a strong fist when necessary. He was the first person to be truly kind to me, a wild-haired orphan girl brought to Palace Lapis after being caught fortune telling. Now, Timos was gone, snatched from life by an assassin's blade that I had completely failed to foresee. It shattered my heart to fail such a man once. Now, staring at the three young people before me, I realized I was about to fail him a second time.

Emperor Timos had only three children eligible for the throne. My eyes fell on Timos's eldest, Bronor. He was handsomely charismatic, with a chiseled face, broad shoulders, and a quick laugh. Bronor was the only heir stupid enough to attempt to sweeten me up, hoping if he used his charm to make me favor him, the elements would favor him too. With his hands clasped as they were, I could see the bruise I'd whacked on his frisky wrist with my fan. The brute was not fit for his dog to lick.

Bronor caught me looking at him, fire kindling in his eyes as he shifted his fingers to cover the bruise. He caught my gaze and held it, refusing to let me look away in an obvious attempt to intimidate. The standoff was thankfully broken by the door screeching open to admit one last occupant.

Carrying a tray with a royal contract and writing utensils, a page came puffing in last, accidentally charging into Councilor Jonse. The jeweled ink bottle on the boy's tray hurled through the air and buried itself in the Councilor's robes, a black stain spreading faster than blood.

Councilor Jonse, usually an even-tempered man, curled his lip in disgust as the page boy shrank away, messy dark hair falling over miserable blue eyes.

Dismissed, whispered the winds. My mind burned with the future image of a bright, blue-eyed pageboy shuffling down the Palace walk in shame. *The boy will be dismissed by Councilor Jonse himself without pay or reference. The child will have to steal to survive.*

"The boy stays," I blurted, more harshly than intended, setting off thunderous echoes and surprised looks. I waited for the echoes and surprise to still and then continued. "I need him to, er, hand me my fan at the proper moment."

Trembling, the page boy shuffled up to my side. I placed my ceremonial fan on the tray beside the heir's contract, saying softly, "Mind you don't get ink on me. I can't undress without two ladies and a trained yellow-faced monkey to help me."

The page boy almost smiled, a flash of intelligence in his eyes convincing me he was no longer afraid of me. I would see to it that the little fellow was not dismissed afterward.

Forgetting the servant, I walked forward until I was facing the emperor's three children, heart pounding in my chest. In the week since the assassination, I'd been sifting the winds of fate, both future and past, to try and determine which heir to choose. All I had learned from fate gave me no hope for anything but a disastrous ending, let alone a happy one, but I had to do my duty.

So I said the required words, "High Prince Bronor, Prince Nenric, and Princess Jarise, you present yourselves here of your own free will, each swearing your claim to the throne is wholehearted and genuine?"

"Yes," the siblings said in well-trained unison.

I continued gravely, "We acknowledge your departed sibling, Erik, who died in infancy and therefore cannot make a claim. As the only other blood-children of the Most Exalted Emperor Timos, I see your claims and honor them, as I honored your Emperor before you."

The two princes bowed properly, and the princess curtsied. With a pang of empathy, I realized Princess Jarise had been crying. Her wavy, black hair was limp, her oval face pale as a white rose except for her bloodshot eyes.

They are orphans, I thought suddenly. *Just like me. First, the Empress died in childbirth, and then a poisoned knife ended their father's life. How unfair fate can be.*

"I will now read the winds," I said, shoving the words past the despair like a boulder clogging my throat. "Your Highnesses, please ponder the future that may be before you."

Obediently, Prince Nenric and Princess Jarise bowed their heads. Prince Bronor stared at me almost insolently, absently rubbing his bruise.

I ignored the eldest son, looking first to the youngest child of Emperor Timos, Princess Jarise. She looked like a goddess except for her freckles and a nose a little too large for deity. Her mouth was full and generous.

Jarise would have made a wise-hearted queen, just like her mother, the fiery Empress Mara. There was common sense in her, and if we hadn't been confined by our stations, Jarise and I could have been friends, the princess being a year my junior. Yet I knew things about Jarise even she didn't know, and as I stared at her grief-stricken face, the death gong of her future tolled in my mind.

Barren, whispered fate. *She has the heart of a mother but not the body. Incurable. She will never produce an heir.*

That pathway led to naught but civil war when Jarise failed to have children. The wind carried the terrible, inevitable sound of the war drums. Shivering slightly, I fought to keep my expression still as I turned to Jarise's next-oldest brother, Nenric. He had the look of a poet and a dreamer, pale with a delicate chin but bright eyes, like his father's.

Weak, the wind gasped in my ear. *The boy was born both a good man and a coward. Though his bright soul and great integrity would force him to action, his body and mind would fail him when faced with the bloody brutality of war. The Empire would fall in less than a lifetime.*

I heard the cries of thousands, the anger of armies, and the despair of Nenric, unable to find the strength to help his country. Hastily, I pulled my mind away from that particular wind of fate, and turned away from Nenric, inwardly mourning and celebrating the man that he was.

Now my eyes fell on Bronor. He had never ceased brashly staring at me, and I hated that he had his kind father's eyes. Warnings against the eldest had been brushing against my mind all week, even if he hadn't already betrayed his lack of integrity to me personally.

Arrogant, chimed the incorrigible wind. *With a seed of madness. If he had chosen to be humble in his position, the madness would not have surfaced until near his death. Yet he has chosen the path of pride, and it will soon be his sanity's downfall.*

"As well as the Empire's," I whispered, so softly even the echo couldn't be heard as more than a whisper.

I had known this impossible choice was before me, but I hadn't expected my stomach to be tying itself in nauseating knots, my palms sweating, and my heart swelling with pain and rebellion. No matter what I chose, the Empire would fall. Thousands would die. With Jarise, civil war would tear the country apart when she proved barren. With soft-spoken Nenric, his own unchangeable weakness would prove the death of armies. With Bronor, I would be unleashing a mad tyrant who would destroy the Empire from within.

Hethro, the Grand Sieve before me, had once said, "We alter a future that is already written, and the possibilities we see are known. Though evil has its choices, so does good. What we call fate is simply a Grand Plan in which we play, and there are miracles hiding where one would never expect."

I needed a miracle, but the winds of fate didn't seem to be producing one. I thought of how my predecessor's only public prophecy had failed to come true when the Empress and her infant son had died, and now I was set up to fail just as spectacularly.

Already the nine councilors waiting for their Emperor were shifting uncomfortably, watching me pace in agony. How, oh how could I pick? I would be the executioner of thousands, the young woman who destined a just and prosperous Empire to ruination and death.

Unbidden, the late Emperor's sparkling eyes flashed before my memory. Stinging tears blurred my vision, threatening to overcome me. How could I sentence one of that great man's children to their own execution? How could I condemn them to anguish or insanity with a word? Why did such a good man die such an evil death so soon?

Hopelessness whelmed about me like smoke, choking and bitter, but the sound of the golden doors opening broke me out of my growing panic. The echoing screech of metal against marble made the throne room sound as if a thousand galloping horsemen in armor were screaming through it. Instead of a thousand men, I saw only Councilor Jonse, who had returned to his rooms to change his ink-stained robes for clean ones.

I nearly snorted despite my distress. I liked Councilor Jonse, but he sometimes acted like a vain fool. To miss such an important moment for the sake of his wardrobe!

Urgently, the winds brushed against my mind with a single word: *Traitor.*

I froze. Councilor Jonse, who obviously had expected to enter on a scene of the papers being signed by the new heir, approached me where I stood—an unprecedented breach of etiquette that took my breath away. I wasn't alone in my surprise and outrage. The rest of the councilors' gasps could be clearly heard in the echoing room, but Jonse ignored them all.

"My apologies, Grand Sieve, but it is time to choose," he said with a faint smile.

I stared at him with new eyes, the whisper echoing in my mind as if it were sound: *Traitor.* I remembered long ago, the first time I'd met Councilor Jonse, how the wind had whispered *snake.* At the time, I thought the word couldn't have been connected to the man before me. Even now, Councilor Jonse smiled kindly.

But even cobras smiled.

"Grand Sieve." Councilor Jonse bowed, but didn't raise from

his bow, clearly wishing to force a decision. I realized the subtle manipulation in the gesture, seeing clearly for the first time how the man had used such tactics to control me for years.

Mind whirling, I turned back to the three heirs, more confused than ever. Jarise was crying quietly on one end, and somehow the sight of her tears broke me.

"Enough," I said softly. With fierce determination, I lowered the defenses of my mind, opening myself to the winds with reckless abandon. The winds of fate tore around me with a cyclone's roaring strength, threatening to wear away my sanity and control. For a moment, I was overwhelmed with images and words, whimpering as the wailing overcame me.

Yellow daisies. Laughing peasants and miserable lords. Palace towers glinting with sun. Whispering cloaks against marble. Furious man in silk robes. Scheming and muttering, Councilor Jonse.

It took all my strength to mentally grip the wind that spoke of Jonse and hear what it had to say. I realized with a start that this was a wind of the past.

Councilor Jonse. Sickroom of the dying Empress. Jonse takes baby from his mother, pays gold to the midwife. Midwife lies, lies. Child stays, stays. Child here, here.

With an almost physical jerk, I dropped my defenses, gasping as the winds fell away and my shocked face turned to the page boy standing in the corner. Tripping slightly over my voluminous robes, I marched to the boy, shoving his tray to the marble with a clang like a thunderbolt and grasping his chin in my hand. The boy squirmed in fright, but I held him fast.

"Be still," I told the page boy, brushing away his rough, dark hair. I peered into the boy's eyes. Beneath their fear, they were blue like the north tower, sparkling and bright and wholesome.

Just like his father's.

"Snake indeed," I hissed. Grabbing the page boy's arm, I led him with more force than grace over to Jarise's side, placing him in the lineup of the heirs. Right where he belonged.

"What is the meaning of this?" one of the councilors murmured in awe.

I took a deep breath, feeling dizzy with hope and a sensation of helplessness lifting. "High Prince Bronor, Prince Nenric, Princess Jarise, and Prince Erik. Having been heartlessly stolen at birth and reported dead by none other than Councilor Jonse himself, Prince Erik will now make a claim for the throne if he knows what is good for him."

The page boy, or rather Prince Erik, who had never stopped bowing in his page boy uniform, spoke with steely panic. "Your, er, Grandness—your Excellence—I... You must be sunstruck. My parents were peasants, cousin to the cook. I'm—"

"The emperor lies dead not a fortnight, a Saurin blade between his ribs, and you are pulling page boys forward as heirs?" Councilor Jonse straightened his spotless clothes and said, more coldly than I'd ever heard him speak, "Councilors, I motion to remove the Grand Sieve from her position. In her youth, the pressure has snapped her reason."

I shrunk back in shock at the man's venom, this man who had always been deceptively kind to me. My gaze flicked to the other councilors, some of whom had grown pale.

"How did you know the blade was Saurin?" said a rail-thin man—Councilor Ioka—with an angry quaver. "You were absent from the palace until this morning. The make of the blade was never discussed in your presence."

Councilor Jonse's face betrayed not an ounce of emotion, yet his fingers twitched. "I will not stand here and suffer such slanderous accusations. I will be in the council room, and I urge the council to stop this madwoman before she destroys the Empire."

In a whirl of silks, Councilor Jonse swept from the room, the tortured sound of the scraping doors echoing after him. Before the doors had fully shut, Councilor Ioka jerked his hand silently at the guards and motioned for the hallway. The guards drew their swords and slipped outside, looking as if they could barely contain their own ire.

As the guards vanished, Councilor Ioka stepped forward and cleared his throat. "Grand Sieve, we still don't have an heir. This boy is truly Emperor Timos's son, believed to be dead?"

I could only nod and swallow hard, trying not to think of the traitor Jonse being carried bodily to the dungeons. "He is indeed, Councilor. I—I will now read the winds. To determine the heir."

Councilor Ioka watched me, inscrutable for a moment, then stepped back. "Just so."

Doesn't care, whispered the wind. *Ioka doesn't care if the boy is a false heir. He saw your earlier despair and knows the boy might be the Empire's only hope.*

Mentally shoving away this insight into Councilor Ioka's thoughts, I turned to the still-frightened boy, not bothering to listen to the winds for the eldest three again. Staring at the boy's face, captured by his eyes, I watched him carefully, sifting through the winds. At last, the answer came, just as terrible as the rest of his family's fates.

The boy is too used to being kicked and bullied. He will lack the confidence to quell dangerous rumors and take his father's place. Evil men will outmaneuver him in a game he never learned to play. He will be ruined before he can bring about the prosperous future he was capable of creating for all his people, noble and serf.

I lowered my barriers, desperate to learn more, something

that would resurrect the brief hope I had felt. What the winds hissed only made it worse. *He will not live to twenty-five, dying in one of his brother Bronor's mad rages. The boy's someday lover, a sweet young laundress, will never recover from his loss, and neither will the Empire.*

I shut my mind off from the winds, stepping back and heaving a shuddering breath. Oh, I had hoped that fate had picked this boy to be here this day so that mercy and goodness could win, and I would not be an executioner before my twentieth birthday. Yet here I was, with no path to pick that didn't end in sorrow.

It was such a travesty. Beneath his white-faced terror, I could see the goodness fairly oozing from the dazed boy, even as the sadness and mischief of thwarted potential threatened to extinguish it. He was noble and good and without undue pride, just like his father. Yet Erik was doomed already thanks to my actions and the actions of nefarious men before me. It was hopeless.

The soft sound of rustling fabric tore my eyes away from the youngest prince. Princess Jarise placed an arm around Erik's shoulders protectively, squeezing gently. The page-boy-turned-prince jumped then looked up at her, wonder on his face.

"Is he really my brother, Grand Sieve?" Princess Jarise said with quiet fierceness, eyes still red and puffy as they burned into mine.

I stared at her, a new idea blooming in my mind. I listened carefully to the winds swirling around the princess and her brother. In the winds' whispers, I had my answer.

I couldn't hold back a brief grin of giddy joy but managed to smother it solemnly before saying, "Princess Jarise, I hereby declare you heir to the emperor's crown, and AS SUCH—" I almost yelled over the ensuing murmurs of echoing surprise, "you must first swear to peacefully abdicate the throne to Prince Erik when he turns seventeen, training him from this moment to rule in your father's place when his youth and inexperience are no longer an issue. If you do not swear and act in this manner, you will bring about the Empire's utter destruction. Do you so swear?"

Princess Jarise's face lit with relief and happiness. I could see in her face as if the words had been painted in ink on her forehead: *I never wanted to be Empress.* "I so swear, Grand Sieve, on my father's honor. Indeed, I will serve my brother until my dying day, if it benefits the Empire."

I nodded. "That would be best. Prince Nenric—"

The dreamy prince stiffened, and I listened to the winds before saying, "Prince Nenric, you should take over the cultural needs of the country that have been neglected. Commission new works of music and literature, and consider starting a library. Lastly, Prince Bronor—"

I saw the man shifting arrogantly, his demeaning sneer cast over his brothers, his pride the only thing forcing his tongue to be still.

If he goes riding on the morrow, the Empire survives, whispered the winds.

"Ride out to search for your father's assassin on the morrow," I said sternly to Bronor, hiding my own confusion at the odd injunction. "And trust me when I say, your fate is both happiest and your service most meaningful on this path."

All of Timos's children bowed or curtsied, astonishment, joy, relief and fury on their faces depending on the child. Tradition dictated that Jarise sign the papers immediately, and knowing the contract wouldn't interfere with the Princess's promise, I allowed her to pick up the quill, dip it in a new ink bottle held by Councilor Ioka, and sign her name. Yet as I watched the happy

Princess, I listened to the winds of fate whisper her future as well as the Empire's.

Princess Jarise is beloved and well-known by the court. None will object to her receiving the throne, even if that throne is temporary. Jarise's natural gift as a mother and strength as a woman will bring her great happiness caring for Erik.

I dove deeper on that particular wind, hoping to hear more.

Jarise knows the subtleties of court and will guide Erik through them, while her goodness means she will gladly give Erik the scepter when the time is right. There is an adventure in Jarise's future, and Erik will sweeten the sadness she will discover when her barrenness becomes apparent.

"Do you know what your predecessor's prophecy was?" Councilor Ioka asked abruptly as Jarise signed the last page.

His voice pulled me away from the whisperings of the wind. I shook my head, still marveling, and replied, "His prophecy was something about the Empress and her last son. Hethro never explained, seeing as he saw that prophecy as his greatest failure."

Councilor Ioka bowed his head. "Grand Sieve Hethro prophesied the Emperor's fourth child would solidify the Emperor's dynasty and secure peace for centuries to come. Councilor Jonse must have seen the child as the end of all his hopes, no doubt hoping as High Councilor that in the case of a civil war, he could seize power. It seems fate is not so easily thwarted."

Another councilor overheard Jonse's last words and added, "I'll bet Jonse had no idea the child still lived. Bless that midwife and curse her."

I smiled and nodded, teary and ridiculous when I was supposed to seem grand and knowing as I watched Jarise gently take her brother Erik's hand (though he held it reluctantly) and lead him from the room. There would be explanations and self-doubt to be worked through, but Erik would conquer himself. The boy had a destiny to fulfill.

The ceremony being over, everyone shuffled for the exit, Bronor storming loudly from the room in a rage, his handsome face twisted. Nenric seemed to shrink before the man's violence as if the younger brother's gentle soul was unable to face such harshness with any kind of fortitude.

So it was that Prince Nenric and I were the last people in the throne room, the guards having not returned from their arrest. The last echoes were beginning to fade when Prince Nenric pressed his slim lips together, crossed to me, and bowed deeply, taking my hand in a respectful gesture.

"My gratitude, Grand Sieve," he said quietly, one chestnut lock of hair falling over his lowered eyes. "You have saved my family and my kingdom, judging by your initially woeful expression when faced with us three. On my father's behalf, I thank you."

Scrambling for some kind of appropriate response to his sincerity, I mentally reached out to the wind for inspiration.

You will love him soon, as he already loves you. In the wind, I saw Nenric watching me at past state functions, a distant smile on his lips. Prompted by the breeze, I remembered conversations when I'd been too nervous speaking to a prince to note the softness of Nenric's gaze as he listened to me stammer.

Jumping as if stabbed, I felt color seep into my cheeks. Mind whirling with unseen possibilities, I held Nenric's broad hand a little tighter, surprised at how little I wanted to let go. "I performed my duty, your Highness, and nothing more. Only I think—I think you should call me Arissa."

Only one more snippet needs to be shared, I think. The following day, Bronor was thrown from his horse after whipping it, and the prince was paralyzed from the waist down. I was shocked and horrified, but the High Prince was humbled by his helplessness to a depth that surprised me. In his humility, Bronor found some measure of happiness and the madness never seized him entirely, nor did he seriously harm another.

Fate was kind to me as well, but that is another wind entirely.

22

About the Authors

Amanda Barusch lives in the American West, where she spends as much time as possible on dirt paths. She has an abiding disdain for boundaries and adores ambiguity. Her work has appeared in *Crack the Spine, Every Day Fiction, Flashes of Brilliance*, and elsewhere.

You can find her on Twitter: @amandabarusch or on her website: http://www.amandabarusch.com.

Cherie Butler has loved writing since grade school. While not being limited to a certain genre, prose and creative non-fiction have been her style of choice. The power of the pen to write on anonymous hearts continues to inspire her writing. She currently lives in the Washington, D.C. Metropolitan area.

Jayrod P. Garrett longs for a world that sees each of us as human beings. As a part of the Black Lives Matter movement he lost friends and some he considered family for the cause. Every sacrifice made him stronger. His goal as a writer and performer is to share art that moves us, as people away from the caricatures that our biases and systems determine others to be, onward to a place where we see each human being for all of who they are.

He's published work in local anthologies and as the co-founder of the Utah Black Artists Collective (UBLAC) and he's editing a collection of poems titled "Being Black in a White Space" to be published and presented hopefully with performances from other members of UBLAC. He is a poet and aspiring fantasy author that graduated from Weber State with his Bachelor of English with an Emphasis on Creative Writing in 2014. He'll be starting graduate school in the fall of 2021 at Sierra Nevada University, in Incline Village, Nevada, for a Master of Fine Arts in Creative Writing with a fiction concentration. Having lived in Utah most of his life he's an Ogdenite at heart, through currently lives with his wife and two kids in Bountiful, Utah.

Krystal C. Gerber writes compulsively and luckily gets paid for it. She is a curriculum writer for a character education company and before that a radio producer with BYURadio. With the League of Utah Writers, Krystal won first place in Romance, Spiritual Essay and Flash Fiction, as well as second place twice for Speculative Fiction and Honorable Mention for New Writer and Poetry. Krystal has been published for three years in a row with LUW Press. She's currently suffering trying to learn French and would appreciate distractions from readers. You can connect with Krystal on Facebook @authorKrystalGerber, on Twitter @krystalcgerber, or through email at krystalgerb@gmail.com

. . .

The League of Utah Writers has been **Claudene B. Gordon**'s support group throughout many writing years. She has been president of Wordcraft Chapter, judge for state LUW contests, winner of LUW writing awards, and is a mother of 6 children, grandmother of 22 grandchildren, great-grandmother of 5. School teacher. Teacher/leader NAMI. Pres. Ut. AMI/Nat'l

Before becoming an English and Journalism teacher, **Donna Graves** was a freelance writer and wrote a personal column for a *The Jordan Valley Sentinel*. Since retiring from the Granite School District, she has enjoyed writing novels and short stories. After attending a Writers at Work workshop at Westminster College in Salt Lake City, she wrote *The Diplomat's Bride*, a novel set in Ceylon where she lived for two years. Her second novel, *Danika's Story*, is set in Sri Lanka, the country once known as Ceylon. "Missing Margaret" is the first of a collection of short stories she is writing.

Kam Hadley is a gender non-conforming Christian and mother of five. Kam is most known for the short story "Accepting Taylor" found in the anthology *Within Earshot: Rumors, Whispers, and Lies*. Email Kam at kamhadleywrites@gmail.com

Josie Hume is the author of several published short stories and articles including *Chasing Tomorrow, The Cottage, Waiting for You*, and *Raising Kids*. Her love affair with writing started at an early age. Her first work was a Christmas play written on an old typewriter and performed by her siblings. Since then, she's enjoyed writing about her modern-day pioneer up-bringing, her year abroad, her adventures in the Marine Corps, and the continuing romance of a wonderful life. When she's not writing, she's doing "mom jobs" with and for her five children, traveling with her husband, or curled up with a good book.

You can find her at josiehume.com.

Lorraine Jeffery has a bachelor's degree in English, a MLIS in library science, and has managed public libraries in Texas, Ohio and Utah. She has won poetry prizes in state and national contests and published over a hundred poems in various journals and anthologies, including *Clockhouse, Kindred, Calliope, Ibbetson Street, Rockhurst Review, Orchard Street Press, Bacopa Press, League of Utah Writers, Two Hawks, Riverfeet, Regal Publishing,* and *Naugatuck River Review.* Her short stories and essays have appeared in many publications, including *Persimmon Tree, Focus on the Family, Mature Years, Elsewhere* and *League of Utah Writers Anthologies.* She is the mother of ten children (eight adopted) and lives in Utah with her husband.

Grace Diane Jessen resides in Glenwood, Utah, with her husband, Gordon. They are the parents of seven daughters and have 18 grandchildren. Diane is an honorary lifetime member of the League of Utah Writers and also a member of the Utah State Poetry Society. Many of her poems have been published and have received state and national awards.

· · ·

Sue Stevenson Leth retired from two successful careers, one in higher education, Weber State College, the other in private business, Celaya Stevenson Design associates, to retire in a warmer climate—St. George, Utah. Membership in in Heritage Writers Guild, Redrock Writers, Dixie Poets, and the League of Utah Writers has given her opportunities to pursue writing poetry and publishing. She acted as executive director for the St. George Literary Arts Festival and recently published for Washington County *The Art of Isolation—An Anthology.*

C. H. Lindsay is an award-winning poet & writer, housewife, and book-lover. She currently has short stories and poems in twelve anthologies, with two more coming out next year. Her works have appeared in several magazines, including *The Leading Edge: A Magazine of Science Fiction and Fantasy, Amazing Stories,* and *Space and Time Magazine.* She is working on three novels, five short stories, and two dozen poems (so far). In 2018 she became her father's literary executor. She now publishes his four books under *Carlisle Legacy Books, LLC,* with plans to add more books in the coming years. She is a member of SFWA, HWA, SFPA, and LUW. She is a founding member of the Utah Chapter of the Horror Writers Association.

M.H. Lopez is a poet, editor, and nature-lover living in San Francisco, CA. He is an editor at Mumber Magazine, and is a co-founder of Lone Mountain Literary Society, a group of artists and writers that produce a literary magazine and host writing events in the Bay Area. Check out his creative-writing column, *Driftwood,* at sfrichmondreview.com.

. . .

He posts his previously published work on Instagram at mhlopez.poetry, & on Twitter @MHLopez_Poetry

Vicky Oliver wrote and published six how-to books for the stressed-out corporate professional under her own name including *Bad Bosses, Crazy Coworkers, and Other Office Idiots* (Sourcebooks, 2008). Under her pen name, Diana Forbes, she wrote and published a novel, titled *Mistress Suffragette* (Penmore Press, 2017). A very active Brown University alumna, Vicky Oliver is enrolled in the Master of Fine Arts program at the New School with an anticipated graduation date of 2022.

Cara O'Sullivan is an editor and writer who lives in Provo, Utah, with her husband and two dogs. She is the mother of a grown son and daughter. Cara has been creating stories and poems since making picture books before she learned to write. She has published poetry and science fiction and fantasy short stories in obscure corners of the universe for more years than she will admit. Cara has a master degree in English from Brigham Young University and works at Utah Valley University as the director of the Policy Office.

David Rodeback lives in American Fork, Utah, works in West Valley City, and writes in any place he can find ten minutes—but the shade of an evergreen tree overlooking Lake Tahoe in the summer is his current favorite.

·　·　·

Elizabeth Suggs is co-owner of the indie publisher Collective Tales Publishing, owner of Editing Mee, and is the author of several stories, two of which were in a podcast and poetry journal. She is the president of two writing groups, one being part of the LUW. And she's a book reviewer and popular bookstagramer. When she's not writing or reading, she's playing video/board games or making cookies.

After a 39-year teaching career specializing in Creative Writing, in retirement **Marie Tollstrup** writes both poetry and prose. While founding and advising *Stylus*, a national award-winning literary/arts magazine for 23 years, her creative flair took root and grew. Currently Marie focuses on poetry, but branches out to articles, short stories, and creative non-fiction which she enters into local, state, and national contests, winning numerous awards for speaking her mind and poetic word play.

Sara Wetmore is an award-winning creative nonfiction author based in Salt Lake City, Utah. She earned her MFA in creative nonfiction writing at Lindenwood University. Her work has appeared in *The Write Launch, At First Glance: An Anthology of Poetry and Prose,* and *Adelaide* magazine. When she is not writing, you can catch her reading a book, sipping on cider off the west coast of mainland Scotland, or playing with her two cats.

Johnny Worthen, (Infinite Monkeys, Salt City Genre Writers, The Usual Suspects) is an award-winning, multiple-genre, tie-dye-wearing author, voyager, and damn fine human being! A

Utah Writer of the Year, trained in literary criticism and cultural studies, he writes upmarket fiction, long and short, mentors others where he can and teaches at the University of Utah.

You can keep up with him at www.johnnyworthen.com where you can join his mailing list and download a free book. What's not to love?

Bryan Young works across many different media. He worked as a writer and producer of documentary films, which were called "filmmaking gold" by *The New York Times*. He's also published comic books with Slave Labor Graphics and Image Comics. He's been a regular contributor for the *Huffington Post, StarWars.com, Star Wars Insider magazine, SYFY, /Film*, and the founder and editor in chief of the geek news and review site *Big Shiny Robot!* He co-authored *Robotech: The Macross Saga RPG* in 2019 and in 2020 he wrote a novel in the BattleTech Universe called *Honor's Gauntlet*.

Made in the USA
Las Vegas, NV
31 July 2021